# FOSSIL HU

## AROUN

# LYME REGIS

# A PRACTICAL INSIGHT INTO
# THE JURASSIC PERIOD

## Written & Illustrated by
## DR COLIN DAWES BSc PhD

© COLIN DAWES STUDIOS
  47 BROAD STREET
  LYME REGIS
  DORSET DT7 3QF
  ENGLAND

ISBN 0-9520112-1-2

Printed by Charles Wheadon

# PREFACE

This booklet follows in the wake of the author's guided fossil hunting expeditions around Lyme Regis. It is geared up to the head of a family or the leader of a group such as school party. Everyone who uses it might well return home with the fossilized remains of sea creatures that lived about two hundred millions of years ago.

Exciting enough. *But before exploring the beaches around Lyme Regis the reader must be aware that the cliffs from which fossils are derived are unstable and going too close to them will put lives in danger. The reader should also bear in mind the danger of becoming trapped by incoming tides.*

For these reasons every sentence which relates to safety has been put in italics. *That said, the casual fossil hunter (unarmed with a geological hammer) should be in no more danger than a beachcomber who heeds warning notices.*

It is hoped that this short publication might interest the qualified geologist exploring the beaches around Lyme Regis for the first time. Such an expert will be critical of many of the sweeping statements which follow but he might forgive the author whose aim is to provide a practical introduction to the Jurassic Period within a few pages and for a reader mostly unfamiliar with technical terms.

Colin Dawes,  Lyme Regis 2003

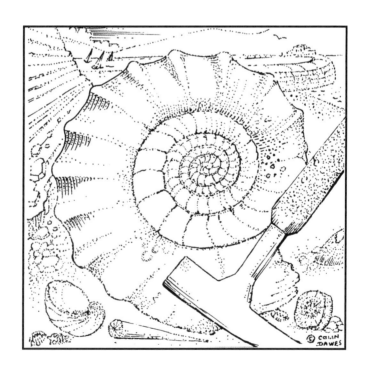

# CONTENTS

# DEDICATED TO PINHAY PAT
### born at Pinhay Farm on cliffs near Lyme Regis
### &
# To all Participants of
# The Author's Fossil Hunting Expeditions

**AUTHOR :**

" Hamish, you are eight years old and we will soon be back in Lyme Regis after a successful two-hour fossil hunting expedition. You have impressed us with your knowledge. You told us that the huge shells we saw on the beach are called ammonites because they resemble the curled horns of Ammon, the ram-headed god of the ancient Egyptians. You pointed out that this is a most unusual name bearing in mind that the jargon of the fossil hunter is based largely upon Greek and Latin. You reminded us that the word dinosaur comes from the Greek words for terrible lizard.

On top of all this, you have collected fossils so tiny that none us could see them before you picked them out of the shingle. And your fragment of a kind of stalked starfish – which you correctly identified by its Latin name as *Pentacrinites fossilis* – was a winner!

By Jove, Hamish, how on earth do you do it?"

**HAMISH :**

"I make a habit of studying ants".

*This little genius had already leant one of the "secrets" of the successful fossil hunter – a good pair of eyes. He had chosen a good place too. The beaches around Lyme Regis are world famous for Jurassic fossils.*

# BACKGROUND

## WHY LYME REGIS ?

The Jurassic formations of England consist largely of deposits laid down in seas. These sediments stretch beneath the soil in a broad diagonal band from west Dorset to north-east Yorkshire. It is possible to find Jurassic fossils in quarries along this band but these excavations are few and far between and you will need permission to enter them.

The richest hunting grounds are situated at each end of the band where seas are cutting into it and forming cliffs from which the fossils are released on to beaches. Consequently, the coastal resorts of Lyme Regis to the south and Whitby to the north have become world famous as centres for geologists and fossil hunters alike.

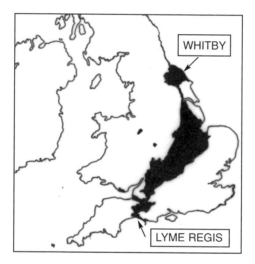

The Jurassic Band of England

English folklore about the origin of ammonites is firmly centred on Whitby where tradition has it that Saint Hilda fashioned them out of snakes that infested her abbey. However, for the holiday-maker with a passing interest in fossils, Lyme Regis might have the edge on Whitby simply because of its warmer location! He would also be following the footsteps of Mary Anning (1799 -1847) perhaps the world's best known fossil hunter. Of humble origins, Mary was born in Lyme Regis where she spent her life collecting fossils which she then sold to the gentry. Her clients included the leading geologists of her day.

For the serious student of the Jurassic Period the beaches around Lyme Regis are a natural starting point because they were the subject of detailed research by William Dickson Lang (1878 -1966). His studies have never been surpassed and are superb examples of what can be achieved with a good pair of eyes and the judicious use of a geological hammer.

But why the band and why is it so good for fossils? To answer these questions we must forget any conception of England as we know it today and picture an arid continent – much of it desert – in which the remains of animals and plants stood little chance of preservation. The onset of the Jurassic Period coincided with the flooding of this continent by encroaching seas about 200 million years ago. The remains of sea-creatures became buried in the sediments that piled up on the sea-floor. These sediments accumulated over a vast period of time and formed a huge layer over the old continent.

Since then there have been many upheavals of the Earth's crust and wide fluctuations in sea level. These factors have contributed to the complex atlas of today in which the British Isles stand out for their great variety of geological formations and in which a swathe of Jurassic sediments has survived as part of the land we call England.

Sands of the ancient continent are exposed as red cliff faces along the east coast of Devon. The sands are carried beneath sea-level towards the Devon/Dorset border and for many miles onwards the cliffs are made up of maritime deposits rich in the fossilized remains of sea-creatures. These are released in profusion on to the beaches but most of them are fragmentary and in order to identify them you will need to have a good idea of what Jurassic sea-creatures looked like and to picture the environment in which they lived.

When reptiles ruled the waves. A fanciful reconstruction of an event during the earlier part of the Jurassic Period, based upon fossils found around Lyme Regis and nearby Charmouth. A dinosaur (*Scelidosaurus*) has been washed out to sea, attracting scavengers.

# JURASSIC SEA-LIFE

Imagine a warm and muddy sea nearer to the equator than Lyme Regis is today. It is two hundred million years BC and the world is dominated by fantastic reptiles. Dinosaurs are roaming around on the nearest land and winged reptiles are gliding overhead.

Other reptiles are swimming. Some of them are good divers and have a superficial resemblance to the dolphins of today. We call them **Ichthyosaurs** from a combination of the Greek words for fish and lizard. Other reptiles (**plesiosaurs** —meaning nearer to lizards) swim in the manner of lumbering turtles. Most of them have long necks. They paddle on the surface, occasionally flicking their heads beneath the water.

All these reptiles are hunting for mobile shellfish that have tentacled heads similar to those of the squids and octopuses of today. This prey is made up largely of **ammonites** and **nautiloids** (both with external shells) and **belemnites** (with internal shells). The belemnite has a body shaped like a bullet and its name is derived from the Greek word for this missile. There are plenty of fish about too but the shellfish are easier targets for the reptiles.

The dung of the reptiles accumulates on the seabed. The fossilized forms of this excrement are known politely as **coprolites** and are important because they contain the indigestible remains of prey (such as fish scales) without which we would know little about the food of ancient marine reptiles.

All sorts of other remains build up on the sea-floor, including **drift wood** and, exceptionally, **the carcasses of dinosuars** swept into the sea. These bits and pieces mingle with debris derived from the shells of creatures that lived on and within the seabed. These shellfish include not only those which are familiar to everyone as oysters and the like, but also other two-shelled creatures which are totally unrelated to them and which we call **brachiopods** (meaning arm-footed, the arm being a curled rake which projected out from between the shells and sifted microscopic food from the sea). Other remains consist of the platey hard parts of stalked relatives of starfish which we call **crinoids** (from the Greek word for lily after the superficial resemblance of these creatures to plants.)

Most of these remains either rot away or are eaten by scavengers but some get buried in the mud where they are preserved as fossils. This mud, containing a patchy record of ancient sea-life, builds up year after year for millions of years during the Period we call Jurassic after similar sediments which now make up the Jura mountains of Europe.

Throughout this vast period of time the sediments move slowly northwards, carried on the shifting plates which make up the Earth's crust. Lyme Regis is built upon these sediments and the seas of today are cutting into them, forming grey cliffs which reveal a cross section of Jurassic history and from which fossils are washed out on to the beaches.

# VIEWING THE CLIFFS

Although Jurassic fossils are plentiful on the beaches around Lyme Regis most of them are mixed up with sand, mud and shingle. It follows that half the secret of finding the fossils is to know what not to look for. This requires a working knowledge of the structure of the cliffs from which the material on the seashore is derived.

You can take in the make-up of the cliffs at your leisure from the Cobb, an ancient and massive breakwater that projects out to sea from the western extremity of the town and which partly encloses its tiny harbour.

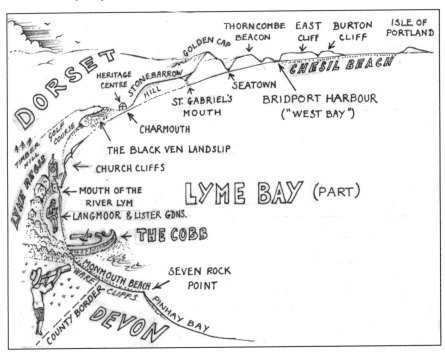

Schematic illustration (not to scale) of coastal features around Lyme Regis, looking roughly eastwards. All the cliffs are visible from the Cobb with the exception of those of Pinhay Bay.

From the Cobb on a clear day you will have a splendid view of the grey sweep that forms the base of the cliffs from Monmouth Beach to beyond Seatown and which consists of sediments laid down in early Jurassic seas. These exposures are world famous and make up part of what has become known as the "Jurassic Coast" of England. Ancient rivers have eaten into the sediments, carving out valleys. Today these rivers are mere trickles but where they enter the sea they provide access points to the Jurassic Coast. The principal ones are: the mouth of the River Lym (pronounced and sometimes spelt Lim) about which the town of Lyme Regis has grown up; the mouth of the River Char; and the mouth of the River Winniford where the hamlet of Seatown is situated. Each of them is easily accessible via branch roads off the A35, the main road which skirts the coast a mile or two inland.

# JURASSIC SEDIMENTS

The sediments containing the most sought after Jurassic fossils stretch from Pinhay Bay to Seatown. They make up what is known as the Lower Lias, the first major subdivision used by geologists in describing the sequence of Jurassic deposits:–

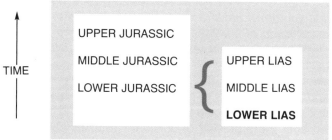

Variations in the nature of the Lower Lias have given rise to distinctive bands of varying shades of grey which form a convenient basis for further subdivision:–

| NAME OF SEDIMENT<br>& notable shell-fish | APPEARANCE |
|---|---|
| GREEN AMMONITE BEDS<br>Ammonites containing greenish crystals | Light grey |
| BELEMNITE MARLS<br>Belemnites, particularly at the top | Light grey with white bands |
| B LACK VEN MARLS<br>A variety of well preserved ammonites | Dark grey to black |
| SHALES - WITH - BEEF<br>Crushed ammonites common<br>Well preserved ammonites at the top | Dark grey to black |
| BLUE LIAS<br>"Giant ammonites" | Alternating bands of dark and pale grey |

We shall consider each of the sediments in detail when we confront them on the beaches but first we must note a quirk of nature which is of enormous benefit to the fossil hunter.

# THE JURASSIC TILT

If the Lower Lias had stayed put then the Jurassic Coast might have been the face of a mountain up which we would have to climb in order to build up a sequence of Jurassic fossils. Instead, the lias has tilted towards the east bringing its strata to beach level one after the other – not unlike a tilted pack of cards.

*It follows that you never have to climb the cliffs around Lyme Regis to acquire a representative collection of early Jurassic fossils; you simply explore the beaches from west to east, picking up progressively younger fossils that have been washed out of the cliffs.*

For example, looking eastwards from the Cobb the Belemnite Marls is visible as a light grey band high in the cliffs of Black Ven and the western side of Stonebarrow Hill from which it slopes down to the foot of Golden Cap and beyond. The Belemnite Marls is named after the profusion of belemnite remains contained within its hard calcium-rich clay (marl). Belemnites can turn up anywhere along the beaches but the best place to find them is from beneath Golden Cap towards Seatown.

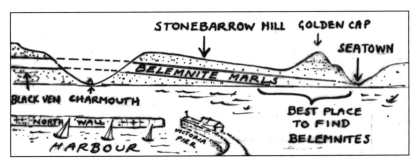

Coastal features (schematic) to the east of the Cobb. The dashed lines indicate the rough position of the Belemnite Marls before this formation was eroded away.

This tidy description of the Jurassic Tilt is very much an over-simplification. Everywhere along the coast the various layers that make up the Jurassic sediments are obscured by mud flows and rock falls, and should the cliffs remain stable for any length of time they soon develop a cloak of vegetation. It is also worth noting that tricks of perspective can distort and even eliminate our appreciation of the Tilt as we explore the beaches close at hand. It is only when you take a boat trip and view the cliffs from a distance that its full significance becomes obvious.

Ancient Earth movements have resulted in the formations arching up here and there along the coast and in places whole sections have slipped. But these events are the concern of the geologist rather than of the casual fossil hunter and we should now turn our attention to the yellow sediments that cap the cliffs like a blanket. These deposits contain plenty of fossils but these were derived from sea-creatures that lived long after the Jurassic Period. The fossils are nothing like as spectacular as those of Jurassic origin but it is important that we consider their origin in some detail if only, as it were, to eliminate them from our enquires.

# THE CRETACEOUS BLANKET

The tilted Jurassic sediments were raised relative to sea level and then mowed down by the elements during a period of many millions of years. The bevelled surface formed a platform upon which the deposits of later seas were laid down. At first these deposits were sandy as they took in grinded sediments derived from land, but as the seas became clearer vast amounts of calcium carbonate were precipitated. Much of this mineral was derived from the shells of floating micro-organisms. Later on it all became compacted into the white rock we call chalk. It is from the Latin word for chalk (creta) that the Cretaceous Period is named, the Period that succeeded the Jurassic and ended with the extinction of the dinosaurs and ammonites.

At one time most of southern England was covered with chalk. This has been worn away along the west coast of Dorset but remnants of the earlier sandy deposits (which belong to the Cretaceous Period ) have survived as cappings on the hill tops. The sand is laden with a green mineral called **glauconite**. For this reason the deposits are known as the Greensand Formation, or more correctly the **Upper Greensand** as represented on this part of the coast. Glauconite weathers yellow and this is the colour of the deposits as they appear in the cliff-faces. The Cretaceous deposits are therefore in striking contrast to the grey Jurassic sediments they cover. It is from this contrast that Golden Cap, the highest peak on the south coast of England, got its name.

The bulk of the Greensand is made up of fine sand known locally as **foxmould**. It is topped by a thick band of splintery rock called **chert**. It rests on a layer of bluish sandy clay called **gault**. In places the gault is topped with rows of big sandy concretions known as **cowstones**. It is said that they got their name from sailors who mistook them for cattle grazing on the cliff-slopes.

Everywhere along the beaches around Lyme Regis you will come across Greensand rocks, minerals and fossils that have made their way down from the cliff-tops in the wake of coastal erosion. The yellow sand of the seashore is derived from foxmould; lumps of chert litter the beaches, and in certain areas many of the boulders are cowstones or their fragments. It is worth remembering that without this continual fall of Cretaceous material all the beaches around Lyme Regis would look grey.

Although chalk is missing along the west Dorset coast much of its top-soil is laden with **flint** derived from this formation. The cliffs of east Devon have retained a great thickness of chalk and its flint falls down on to the sea-shore as these cliffs erode. There is a tendency for beach material to drift from west to east in keeping with waves set up by the prevailing south-westerly winds. In this way much flint is channelled all the way along the length of Monmouth Beach where it piles up with chert and rolled fragments of hard Jurassic limestone against the Cobb.

For the "Jurassic purist" all this Cretaceous material gets in the way. Certainly, Lyme Regis can't compete with places elsewhere along the south coast of England (such as Folkestone) as a hunting ground for Cretaceous fossils. For anyone new to fossil hunting the Cretaceous debris is a bonus, however.

*And for safety reasons alone anyone armed with a geological hammer must be wary of flint and chert.*

These rocks are made up almost entirely of **silica**, an extremely hard mineral. Cavities in the rocks are sometimes lined with **quartz**, the crystalline form of silica. A bubbly form of quartz known as **chalcedony** (pronounced *kal – said – ony*) is not uncommon. The bubbles range in size from that of a pin head to a grape. They often feel waxy and can be of almost any colour according to the nature of impurities. The bluish kind has gained a fine reputation as a collectable mineral and is known as Lyme Bay Chalcedony. It should be noted that the terms used here for Cretaceous rocks are those used locally. Many authors refer to flint as a type of chert and both rocks are often described as forms of chalcedony.

In spite of their chemical similarity, flint and chert can be readily told apart from their general appearance. Flint is a knobbly rock with a whitish rind and a dark but translucent interior. It can take on all sorts of curious shapes. Small pieces (flint nodules) are often mistaken for fossilized bones and teeth but these are invariably dark grey or black. Chert is blocky and of some shade of yellow or brown. The rocks can also be told apart by the different ways in which they fracture. The surfaces of freshly broken flint are shell-like, whereas those of chert are flat or jagged.

*But in no way use your hammer on these rocks. They break up into razor-sharp splinters that can turn into lethal flying objects. And it is irresponsible to break up these rocks on a beach used by bare-footed holiday-makers during the summer.*

The ability of the splinters to maim and kill was much exploited by our ancestors whose flint and chert implements (mostly scrapers, used to trim hides) often turn up on the seashore where they have tumbled down from the grassy cliff-tops.

The origins of the silica that make up these rocks are obscure but the fossil hunter will gladly accept the popular theory that much of the silica was derived from sea-creatures (for example, sea-urchins) that used it for building up their hard parts. The spineless and heart-shaped carcass of a sea-urchin made up entirely of flint or chert is one of the most coveted of all Cretaceous fossils, fine specimens of which frequently turn up on Monmouth Beach. If you think of a starfish with its five arms pinned up over its back and then imagine the spaces between the arms filled up with spiny hexagonal plates then you will have a good idea of what to look for. Many of the flint specimens are of an urchin called **Micraster**, meaning little star.

Sea-urchin fossils are very much chance-finds and the only well preserved Cretaceous fossils that can always be found around Lyme Regis are the coiled tubes secreted by a worm known as **Rotularia concava**. The tubes are very common in cowstone. They show up well in wet pebbles of this rock even when few of the fossils are present. Conversely, they can be scarcely evident in dry pebbles that are full of them.

The explanation for this disappearing trick is to do with light. Cowstone is made of compacted sand grains which have sufficient gaps of air between them to scatter light. As the stone soaks up water the amount of light reflected from these spaces is reduced in contrast to that reflected from the fossil which is impermeable to water. The same phenomenon applies to the Jurassic fossils made up of calcite and buried in limestone that we shall consider later. Meanwhile it is sufficient to note that the fossil hunter should never be put off by a bit of rain which always works to his advantage!

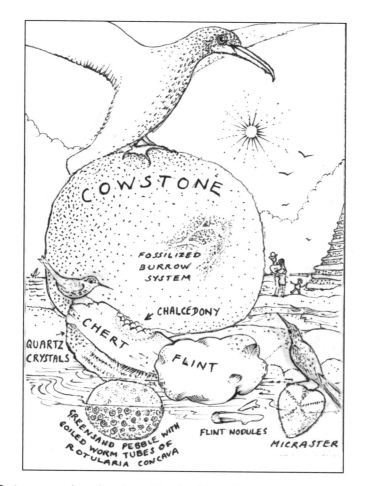

Cretaceous rocks, minerals and fossils of Lyme Regis. The hefty cormorant and the sparrow-sized rock pipit (common local birds) are included for scale.

The sediments which make up the Greensand Formation and Gault are stacked in a roughly horizontal position. It follows that their debris on the beaches will encompass about the same time range wherever you are in contrast to material derived from Jurassic sediments which, because of their tilt, are distributed in such a way that the further east you go the younger are the fossils to be found:–

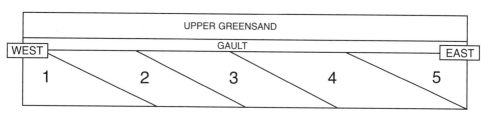

(1) Blue Lias  (2) Shales-with-Beef  (3) Black Ven Marls
(4) Belemnite Marls  (5) Green Ammonite Beds

13

# PREPARING FOR A FOSSIL HUNT

## Sensible precautions

The cliffs around Lyme Regis are crumbling all the time and it is obviously dangerous to go too close to them. Mudflows are frequent and it is said that you could equip an army with the boots left behind by holiday-makers who got stuck! Another hazard is slippery seaweed; beware especially of the green kind that grows profusely on stone slabs. Above all, every fossil hunter must be aware of tide conditions: you can be cut off at bends in the cliffs if you ignore warning signs.

If you are not quite sure what to do (and especially if you have children with you) then consider going on an organised fossil hunt led by a local expert. These tours are available throughout the year and details about them can be obtained from the Lyme Regis Tourist Information Centre.

## What to take

A geological hammer is not essential because water has done the work for you in rinsing fossils out of the cliffs and on to the beaches. Your best asset is a good pair of eyes. That said, a hammer is useful for trimming pieces of rock containing fossils. If you use one then it makes sense to protect your eyes with a visor or goggles and your hands with gloves. A hammer is also useful for giving scale to photographs, particularly when recording the impressions of giant ammonites in boulders.

Plastic bags are convenient for retaining your larger fossils. Polythene sandwich bags are ideal for small and cherished finds; all too often an exquisite specimen is tucked into a pocket from which it falls out. The chances of finding it again amongst the shingle are remote – it is much easier to locate a bag blowing about the beach! A kitchen roll is worth carrying for use in wrapping up and protecting your fossils although ordinary newspaper will do for bulky finds.

A hand lens with a ten-times magnification is needed to appreciate the finer details of the fossils and crystals that we shall consider.

A portable telephone will give you peace of mind but make sure your battery is fully charged!

## What to wear

Strong footware is advisable at any time of the year, otherwise clothing to suit weather conditions is the rule. Never underestimate the chill factor when the wind is blowing from the east during winter. This is often the best time to go fossil hunting, especially after stormy weather when cliff falls are frequent and the shingle is rapidly turned over. It is worth noting that the beaches around Lyme Regis can be surprisingly warm when cold winds are blowing from the north over the cliff-tops.

# What to expect

You might be lucky enough to come back with a "perfect" specimen or two, similar to those on display in museums and fossil shops, but "imperfect" fossils are far more common and are just as good for elucidating the evolutionary sequence of the Jurassic sea-creatures that we are about to consider. When you can identify these creatures from mere fragments of their fossilized remains then you have graduated from a collector of curiosities to a palaeontologist, the name given to a scientist who studies fossils.

Bear in mind that anyone exploring the beaches around Lyme Regis is walking over countless tons of Jurassic and Cretaceous debris that is turned over with every tide and that the fossil hunter is merely scratching its surface. Your chances of finding something spectacular are as good as anyone else's, assuming of course equal knowledge and powers of observation.

# Code of Conduct

Is it all right to collect fossils from the beaches around Lyme Regis ? The simple answer is that if you don't pick up the loose fossils derived from shale then the sea will, crushing them beyond recognition. Some of the biggest names in fossil hunting live in or near Lyme Regis and they face a constant battle in rescuing specimens that would otherwise be pounded into oblivion. Rest assured that you are doing something of a service by keeping your fossils, especially if they are subsequently shown at a school for the benefit of general education. Plastic dinosaurs are fun but those bits of Jurassic history to be picked up around Lyme Regis are the real thing!

When it comes to the cliffs it is a very different story. Cliffs are edges of land and it is understood that anything in them belongs to the owner of that land. Fortunately, the owners are well aware of the need to record specimens before the cliffs succumb to the forces of coastal erosion. It is in this spirit that a code of conduct has been drawn up, copies of which can be procured from The Charmouth Heritage Centre.

# Where to go

There are two major sites for fossil hunting within easy walking distance from the Lyme Regis: Monmouth Beach (to the west of the Cobb) and the beaches to the east of the town (towards Charmouth).

If you are new to the area then explore Monmouth Beach first. *Its fossils are easy to make out and you will be in sight of the Cobb and emergency services.* You will also get to know the tides and become acquainted with the earliest of the Jurassic formations. This approach is adopted here, where the fossils of Monmouth Beach are described in detail before we head towards Charmouth and beyond, taking in progressively younger formations.

*But before setting out it is important to let someone know where you are going and what time you expect to be back.*

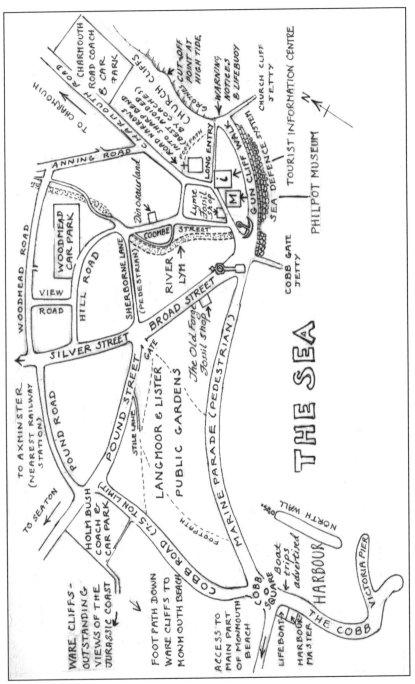

Rough plan of Lyme Regis. For details about accommodation contact the Lyme Regis Tourist Information Center. Several hotels and guest houses have collections of local fossils. Only the major car and coach parks skirting the town on high ground are included. There are several car parks off Broad Street and the road to the west of Cobb Square but these are rapidly filled up during holiday periods.

# EXPLORING THE BEACHES

## MONMOUTH BEACH AND "GIANT AMMONITES"

Monmouth Beach offers a superb introduction to ancient sea-life. With the exception of belemnites, the fossilized impressions of Jurassic shell-fish are extremely abundant. A famous Jurassic oyster known as "The Devil's Toenail" is commonplace and many boulders are festooned with fragments of crinoids. Everywhere there are traces of creatures that once burrowed in the Jurassic seabed or crawled over it. The skeletal remains of swimming reptiles occasionally turn up but above all else the beach is renowned for its huge ammonites contained within slabs of limestone derived from the Blue Lias.

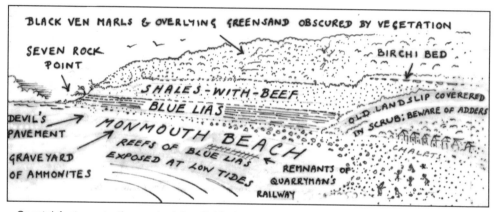

Coastal features to the west of the Cobb. Monmouth Beach is famous for the impressions of giant ammonites on the surfaces of limestone boulders derived from the Blue Lias. Others are massed together in a ledge on the seashore known as The "Graveyard of Ammonites". Not so well known is another ledge (named here "The Devil's Pavement") which is full of the remains of a Jurassic oyster that has been known for centuries as "The Devil's Toenail".

The **Blue Lias** forms the base of the cliff all the way along Monmouth Beach. It looks like a huge multiburger with layers of pale grey limestone for bread interlaced with layers of dark shale (hardened layers of mud) for butter. No one is exactly sure how this peculiar structure arose. It is tempting to attribute the bands to varying conditions during which the seas were either relatively clear or muddy. Alternatively, the limestone might have consolidated into layers during or after the overall deposition of the sediment. Both factors appear to have played a part.

As the cliffs erode, the shale is rapidly dispersed by wave action leaving its tougher fossils trapped amongst the shingle while fragments of limestone persist as boulders. These boulders are rich in ammonites and other fossils and they litter the beach from the base of the cliffs to well below the low tide mark.

*It follows that you never have to go close to the cliffs in search of fossils derived from the Blue Lias. Even at high tide there is usually a wide expanse of shingle exposed at the Cobb-end of the beach where boulders derived from the Blue Lias can be examined in safety.*

17

Moreover, It is to be expected that the shells of dead ammonites settled on the sea-floor along their flat sides like saucers thrown into a bath tub. This is the manner in which most of the shells lie in the cliffs. Consequently, they show up on a cliff-face edge-on and are usually difficult to make out, especially in shale where they are often compressed beyond recognition.

*Searching for ammonites and other fossils in a vertical cliff-face is not only dangerous it is like looking for squashed needles in hay stacks. A needle looked at from above is easy to make out but when viewed end-on you can scarcely see it.*

In contrast, the contours of ammonites as they appeared on the Jurassic sea floor (that is, looking from above) are easy to spot on the surfaces of limestone slabs that have tumbled out the cliffs and well away from them. As you make your way along Monmouth Beach you will soon come across slabs of Blue Lias which are covered with sheets of rather small and compressed shells of ammonites that look like the wheels of toy tractors. They are in striking contrast to other boulders which contain shells that are well over a foot in diameter.

These **"giant ammonites"** can be as big as cartwheels. Allowing for the protruding head and tentacles they might have been as big as carts. The largest known ammonite shell was found in the Cretaceous deposits of Germany. It is about seven feet in diameter and the entire creature was probably as big as a shire horse.

Many ammonites are buried deep within the stone and show up only around its edges. The shells of compressed specimens then appear as crinkled lines whereas the internal structures of large and undamaged shells are revealed in detail. An intact shell of an ammonite that as been exposed across its middle in the manner of a snapped coin gives rise to an impression similar to the outline of a dumbbell. There is often a nipple projecting outwards at either end of the impression. Each nipple usually has a depression on either side of it. From these features we can tell that the outer coil of the shell was larger than the inner ones and that a keel flanked by grooves ran around the rim of the shell. The fossil hunter is very much a detective!

The shells of other big ammonites lie oblique and give rise to all sorts of curious patterns which are sufficient not only to excite the explorer in search of ancient shell-fish but also the artist wishing to depict Nature's curiosities. As one participant of the author's fossil hunting expeditions put it, "You will keep coming across a busy stone!"

*You will be tempted to try and extract these shells but this is a waste of time as they are very much part of the rock. They are worthy of a camera rather than the insult of a geological hammer and should be left alone for others to enjoy.*

The original material that made up the shell has either recrystallised or has been replaced by microscopic crystals of **calcite.** This is the pure form of calcium carbonate – the mineral of which limestone is largely composed. Many of the white lines on limestone are calcite-filled cracks that have nothing to do with fossils. Some of the lines can be traced downwards in the cliffs and over the ledges on the seashore where they evidently represent the edges of sheets of calcite which filled cracks in the sediments long after they were laid down. Limestone slabs frequently split apart around these areas of weakness. When freshly exposed the calcite attracts immediate attention as it sparkles in the sunshine but it is soon worn down by the waves to nothing more than a white patch. You can carry out a crude but effective test for calcite by placing a small sample in a weak acid such as vinegar. It will fizz away to nothing. Try the same thing with a piece of flint containing quartz crystals and nothing will happen.

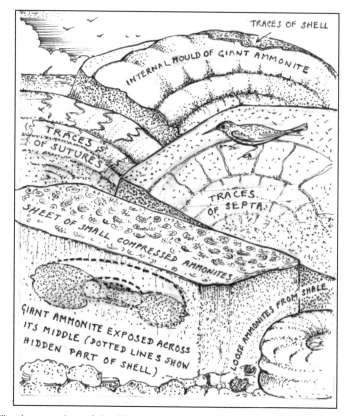

Fossilized ammonites of the Blue Lias. Those buried in limestone are very much part of the stone and it is a waste of time trying to get them out. They make intriguing photographs, however, and illustrate all aspects of the structure of the shell. The ammonites to collect are loose specimens that have been washed out of

Pure calcite crystals look like lopsided diamonds and they can be as big and sharp as dog's teeth, which is their nickname. They are often stained brown or orange by the presence of iron impurities. Patches of small and impure calcite crystals resemble sprinklings of demerara sugar. The grey colour of Lyme Regis limestone can be attributed to the muddy nature of the Jurassic sea-floor and if it were not for this factor then the stone would be as white as chalk and the fossils would be difficult to make out, just as they often are in chalk itself.

The soft parts of ammonites were never preserved and when we say that we have found an ammonite we really mean that we have discovered either its fossilized shell or the hardened substance that filled the shell – its **internal mould.** (Little more than the rare impressions of the outlines of tentacles are all we have to "reconstruct" the living animal).

The interior of the shell was divided by thin walls (septa) into a series of **air chambers** that enabled the ammonite to float. The body of the ammonite occupied the chamber nearest the opening of the shell. As the ammonite grew it sealed up this **body chamber** and moved forwards into a new one of its own making. After the death of the ammonite its rotting tissues were replaced by mud that filled up the body chamber.

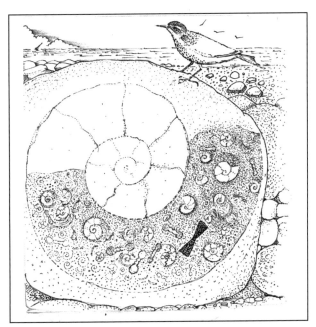

A limestone boulder derived from the Blue Lias containing a giant ammonite in which the body chamber is filled with smaller ammonites and other debris that have been swept in.

The mud which swept into the body chamber of a large ammonite often contained the remains of smaller ammonites which are known to fossil hunters as **body chamber ammonites**. These were commonly mixed up with other debris, notably the shells of Jurassic oysters. Fragments of bone derived from a marine reptile sometimes show up (the dark impression in the illustration is of part of a vertebra split across its middle; we will consider it in more detail later on). Body chambers containing these relics are unique time capsules of Jurassic history and are worthy of your utmost scrutiny. But it is a waste of time trying to extract them from limestone boulders. They come into their own as isolated units washed out of shale; their compacted remains formed a tough unit after the "host shell" had disappeared. Complete units can be recognised by their curved surfaces which delineate the boundaries of the hosts, but such specimens are far from common.

The entrance of mud into the air chambers was restricted if the shell remained intact. This gave space for the development of calcite crystals. You will sometimes come across a broken boulder of limestone in which these cavities are exposed with their linings bristling with "dog's teeth".

The walls between the air chambers of ammonites can be likened to a series of stalkless maple leaves. The edges of each "leaf" crinkled up rather abruptly where they adhered to the interior of the shell not unlike (and perhaps functionally equivalent) to the system of fan vaulting that props up the roofs of many of our churches. These edges frequently show up as a series of squiggly lines on the outer surfaces of internal moulds. The lines resemble those between the bony plates of our skulls and given the same name: **sutures.** They evolved into an extraordinary variety of patterns which are extremely important in telling ammonites apart. But we should note that these markings are nothing more than the impressions of the frilled margins of septa; they are independent of the form and decoration of the shell.

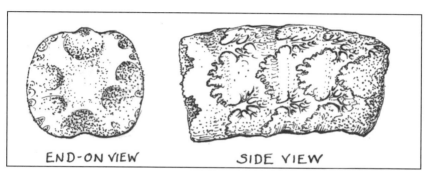

END-ON VIEW          SIDE VIEW

Fragments of the internal moulds of ammonites often split apart about a fossilized wall that abutted an air chamber. The bumps on the wall have an uncanny resemblance to the pads on the foot of a cat, hence the nickname Cat's Paw for this part of the specimen. The fossilized edges of the walls give rise to the suture lines. The patterns depicted here are typical of some of the larger ammonites found on Monmouth Beach.

The shells of many ammonites resemble coils of concertina tubing. The pleats of the tubing are known as **ribs.** The number and form of these ribs varied from one species of ammonite to another. Sometimes they sprouted knobs and even spines. Very often the ribs were interrupted by a **keel** as they ran around the rim of the shell, a feature characteristic of the giant ammonites of the Blue Lias. The **size** of the shell is more difficult to evaluate as a means of telling ammonites apart. Most fossilized shells probably belonged to adults but others were certainly those of youngsters. It is also widely accepted that there were **sex differences.** Although the reproductive organs of ammonites were never fossilized, two distinctive types of shell – large and small, often with different ornamentations – are sometimes found mixed up together. The smaller ones are believed to have belonged to male ammonites and the larger ones to females (to accommodate egg production). But such an assumption is usually avoided by calling them **microconchs** and **macroconchs,** meaning small and big shells respectively.

Loose and complete specimens of huge ammonites derived from shale occasionally show up on the seashore, especially after a major cliff fall, an event certainly to bring local collectors to the scene and with whom you will be in competition. Finding these magnificent specimens is very much about being in the right place at the right time but there is always the chance of finding one that has been missed, sandwiched between boulders low down on the beach.

# "JURASSIC BEEF"

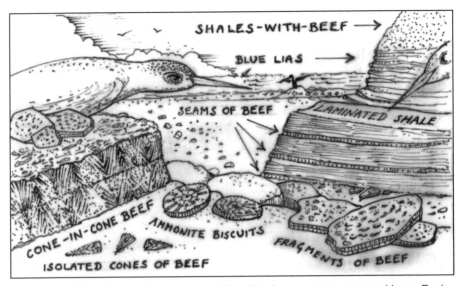

Examples of "beef", a peculiar form of calcite which is very common around Lyme Regis

The Blue Lias is immediately overlain by the Shales-with-Beef. This contains numerous thin bands of limestone which, when cut across, reveal vertical striations not unlike those seen when cutting through a beefsteak and from which the formation gets its name. Much of the shale is made up of paper-thin laminations and thick bands of limestone are few and far between. Consequently, the Shales-with-Beef is inherently unstable and when wet it slides down over the cliff-face, obscuring the details of the Blue Lias.

Each layer of beef is normally made up of two layers. Identical impressions of ammonites often show up on either side of this sandwich, indicating that the rock was formed after the ammonites were fossilized, splitting them across their flat axes. Slithers of beef encapsulating these ammonites ("ammonite biscuits" as I call them) are collectable items but otherwise this rock has little to offer the fossil hunter. Moreover the the surfaces of beef are commonly pitted with impressions which look very much like fossils but are really due to the nature of the rock itself.

The vertical striations of beef consist of tiny cones of calcite crystals that are stacked up like heaps of shuttlecocks. The crystals are too small to be seen with the naked eye but are evident from their reflections when the broken rock is held up to the sun. The cones give rise to circular impressions on either side of the beef and these are sometimes mistaken for ammonites. Thick layers of beef are not uncommon where the shuttlecock arrangement of the calcite becomes obvious. The rock is then known as **cone-in-cone beef**. When exposed across these cones can resemble the interlocking teeth of an Ichthyosaur!

Layers of beef often pile up one on top of the other and when contorted give rise to all sorts of shapes that might be mistaken for fossils. To sum up: every fossil hunter should know about this curious rock if only to avoid it.

# "ARNIES"

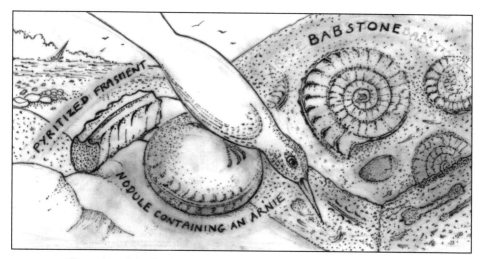

Examples of the fossilized remains of *Arnoiceras* – "arnies" for short.

The characteristic ammonites of the Shales-with-Beef belong to the genus **Arnioceras** and are known to local collectors as "Arnies". They are nothing like as big as the giant ammonites of the Blue Lias (a typical specimen will fit into the palm of your hand) but like them they are adorned with a keel flanked by grooves running around the rim of shell. These features are very pronounced in the Arnie which also sports clear-cut ribs which bend forwards rather abruptly as they approach the keel. In a similar ammonite, *Caenisites,* derived from the overlying Black Ven Marls, the ribs are more rounded. Only the internal moulds of the body chamber of these ammonites are common as a loose fossils. As with most ammonites derived from shale the inner (air filled) chambers have either been flattened beyond recognition or have disappeared altogether. Body chambers are especially attractive when made up of iron pyrite ("fool's gold"), a glittering compound of iron and sulphur.

A dead ammonite acted as a sort of chemical cradle about which many minerals were exchanged as it became buried in mud. The processes involved are still poorly understood. They often led to the formation of a hard nodule encapsulating the shell. A worn nodule with an Arnie or a similar type of ammonite exposed around its edge is a common find on Monmouth Beach.

The Shales-with-Beef contains a band of limestone known as **The Black Arnioceras Bed** (and also as The Hartmanni Bed) which in places is full of intact Arnies. Slabs of this bed fall down on to Monmouth Beach but the rock is usually very hard making it difficult to extract the fossils. But you don't have too – a fragment of **"Babstone"**, as we might call it, will look good in your collection as an example of conditions on the Jurassic sea-floor. The ammonites are usually mixed up, indicating turbulence. The stone often contains black shells of "ordinary" shellfish – bivalved molluscs – creatures that we shall consider in detail later on. Incidently, the names of many Jurassic ammonites end in "–ceras", a derivation from the Greek word for a horn (as in rhinoceros).

# "TORTOISE AMMONITES"

The Shales-with-Beef is topped by a band of limestone which can be seen poking out high in the cliffs towards the Cobb-end of Monmouth Beach. Buried beneath this band and separated from it by a foot or two of shale, is a layer of large nodules. The band, and especially the nodules, contain well preserved ammonites of a species called **Microderoceras birchi,** and the two formations taken together is known as the Birchi Bed. Although this bed is inaccessible the nodules roll down to the sea-shore as the cliffs erode. The typical nodule looks like a rugby ball and is just as big.

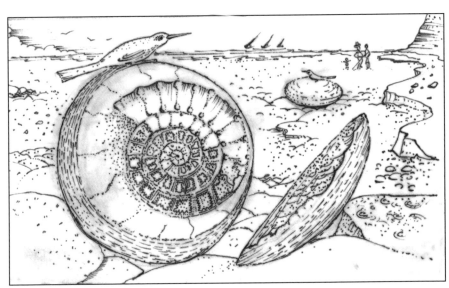

A Birchi nodule broken open to reveal a "Tortoise Ammonite". The fossil formed a natural cleavage plane. *See below for a cautionary note.*

*If you are lucky enough to find one of these nodules then you should think twice before trying to break it open. The stone is very hard and the head of hammer could glance off its rounded surface and cause serious injury* And there is no guarantee that the nodule will contain an ammonite.

The ribs of the *Microderoceras birchi* are widely spaced and each one is adorned with four knobs, a pair on each side of the shell. The air chambers are usually filled with glistening calcite crystals that are stained brown by the presence of iron impurities. The resemblance of the exposed ammonite to a tortoiseshell explains its old nickname.

The Birchi Bed marks the division between the Shales-with-Beef and the overlying Black Ven Marls. Fossils derived from the Marls occasionally turn up on Monmouth Beach but as we shall see the best place to find them is on the other side of Lyme Regis where the formation descends towards sea-level in keeping with the Jurassic Tilt.

# TRACE FOSSILS

Many of the limestone boulders of Monmouth Beach are mottled with dots and streaks of varying shades of grey. For a long time it was thought that these curious patterns were the fossilized impressions of seaweeds. They are still known as fucoidal (pronounced *few*-coidal) markings after the common brown seaweed *Fucus* of today but it is now widely accepted that most of them resulted from activities of worms and other creatures that burrowed into the Jurassic sea-floor.

No one has ever found the fossilized remains of these animals – their soft tissues rapidly rotted away after death – but a number of distinctive burrow systems can be made out and it is a fair assumption that each was made by a different species. Other markings have been attributed to the excursions of crustacea (crabs and their kin) that crawled over the seabed.

In making sense of the patterns you will need to think in three dimensions. For example, a system of dots might represent a cross-section of a complex burrow system made by single animal. And two circular depressions linked by a hazy line could be the flattened trace of a U-shaped burrow once occupied by a Jurassic worm that lived like the lugworm of today that burrows in sandy patches around Lyme Regis and is much sought after by anglers for use as bait.

All these impressions come under the general heading of Trace Fossils. Those to be seen around Lyme Regis are very important for working out conditions on the Jurassic sea-floor but in terms of popular imagination they fade into insignificance when compared with those found elsewhere in Dorset – the impressions of dinosaur footprints. These were, of course, made in sediments on land, swampy mud perhaps, but visitors to Lyme Regis sometimes expect to find them!

A Jurassic wormery? Many of the peculiar markings that adorn slabs of Jurassic limestone (and riddle shale) can be put down to burrowing creatures that altered the texture of the seabed during their activities.

# JURASSIC DRIFTWOOD

Although the impressions of Jurassic seaweeds can be ruled out on Monmouth Beach, bits of Jurassic trees and other ancient fragments of land vegetation are very much in evidence. These remains are widely scattered in limestone and shale and they can be as big as logs, which is what they are, logs derived from trees that were swept into the sea and became buried in mud during the age of dinosuars.

No doubt many of these trees once brushed shoulders with dinosaurs and for this reason alone a splinter of Jurassic driftwood is worthy of your collection even though it will have none of the attractive qualities of your ammonites. A peculiar type of limestone is so full of Jurassic driftwood that it is known as Woodstone. This rock is also very rich in ammonites and is highly sought after. It is seldom found on Monmouth Beach as it situated in the in the middle of the Black Ven Marls, a formation which, as we have noted, is thinly represented in the cliffs on this side of Lyme Regis. The best place to find Woodstone is on the beaches beneath Black Ven where it is washed out from mudflows. It is therefore described and illustrated later on.

The colour of Jurassic drifwood wood ranges from chocolate-brown to charcoal-black. It is often mistaken for fossilized bone which is also very dark but the wood can normally be scratched by your fingernail in contrast to fossilized bone which is invariably hard.

Much of the wood is still friable in the form of lignite. On rare occasions the cliffs catch fire due to the rapid oxidation of iron pyrites, a process which generates a lot of heat, setting fire to the lignite. This last happened in a big way in 1908 much to the joy of visitors and to the benefit of the tourist trade. Lyme Regis was then dubbed "The Naples of England" and it is said that the locals poured paraffin over its "burning mound" to keep the visitors coming.

Limestone boulders often contain wood infiltrated by calcite. When exposed on the surface of the stone the wood is eventually worn away but the network of calcite remains.

It should be noted the Jurassic wood of Lyme Regis is of poor quality compared with that to be found around Whitby where it is known as jet. This rock is easy to carve and takes a fine polish. It was used extensively in the making of jewellry during the reign of Queen Victoria following the death of her beloved husband, Prince Albert.

The Jurassic drifwood found around Lyme Regis is generally too far gone to make out significant structural details, but we know from contemporary deposits laid down elsewhere that Jurassic vegetation was made up largely of conifers, cycads (resembling but unrelated to palm trees), tree ferns (huge extinct relatives of ferns) and tall horsetails (still with us today in a diminutive form).

The flowering trees of today (oaks, elms etc.) did not get going until well after the Jurassic Period. They first appear as fossils in Cretaceous deposits. We should also picture the Jurassic landscape as grassless but ferny. In spite of their simple appearances, grasses are highly advanced plants whose flowers have been reduced to insignificant proportions to allow the rapid dissemination of pollen by wind through which agent they have carpeted vast areas of our planet.

# "THE JURASSIC STAIRCASE"

Every boulder on Monmouth Beach tells a story and we need to think in three dimensions in order to make sense of the extraordinary impressions which often adorn them. The fourth dimension – time – will tax your imagination to the full. Many of the limestone slabs derived from the Blue Lias have tumbled down to the beach from a position high up in the cliffs and have landed upside down, making it difficult to tell which of their surfaces represent bases in time.

Fortunately, we do not need to scale the cliffs in order to study the various layers of which the Blue Lias is composed. Because of the Jurassic tilt each layer forms the base of the cliffs at some point between Pinhay Bay and the Cobb. Moreover, every one of them juts out to sea, giving rise to a series of pavements which can be examined in safety well away from the cliffs. It is these ledges which form the base of the seashore. They make up a sort of staircase which is very evident when looking towards the Cobb from beyond Seven Rock Point.

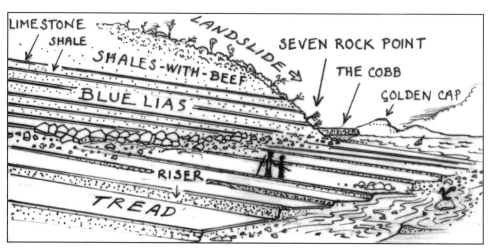

A schematic illustration of The Jurassic Staircase viewed from Pinhay Bay at a good low tide. The "treads" are hard layers of limestone continuous with the bands at the foot of the cliffs. The intervening layers of shale have been eroded away along the seashore, resulting in a series of "risers". The figures are walking eastwards over progressively younger Jurassic formations but their position is maintained roughly at sea level. *Note that they are almost out of sight of the Cobb and emergency services, and that they could be trapped by mudslides.*

The staircase undulates along Monmouth Beach and it is usually obscured by sand and shingle. Even when this debris is cleared away by rough seas most of the "treads" of the staircase look very similar apart from differences in irregularities of their surfaces. But there is one ledge that is unmistakable because it is covered with impressions of big ammonites – as if it were a graveyard for these extinct creatures.

# "THE GRAVEYARD OF AMMONITES"

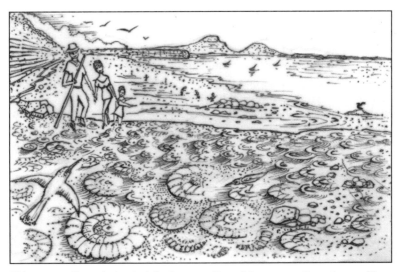

This extraordinary ledge is full of ammonites of the genus *Coroniceras*. They are all part of the stone and can not be extracted individually. It is important that the ledge is left alone for everyone to enjoy and for scientists to study.

This is the local name for a ledge of limestone packed with the internal moulds of ammonites. It is situated just beyond the Dorset/Devon border, projecting from the base of the cliffs at a point about halfway between the Cobb and Seven Rock Point. As you approach it you might well find a large ammonite with one half of its shell in Dorset and its other half in Devon! The average diameter of the graveyard ammonite is similar to that of a football. Many of the moulds stand proud of the stone, giving the graveyard the quaint appearance of a miniature lunar landscape.

The Graveyard is a source of wonder to anyone standing on it and it is certainly a place to let your imagination run wild. No-one knows its exact extent because it disappears into the cliffs in one direction and dips beneath the sea in the other. It puts in a tantalising appearance well down the beach to the south-west of Seven Rock Point where it is mostly obscured by barnacles and other living creatures with hard shells. It is probably very extensive because, as we shall see, it turns up on the other side of Lyme Regis after the dip in the Blue Lias beneath the town.

It is anyone's guess as to why so many ammonites are crammed together. Perhaps the graveyard was simply the result of the accumulation of empty shells derived from generations of ammonites that lived and died. The shells could have been swept into a shallow bay. There is a local reminder of how tides and topography can bring things together; Dead Man's Cove, situated to the east of Golden Cap, got its name from the bodies that were washed into it when shipwrecks were common in Lyme Bay during the days of tall ships. It is just possible that many of the ammonites were exhausted females that died after breeding in shallow waters. A less fanciful explanation is that a vast shoal of inshore ammonites was suffocated by sediments pouring into the sea from rivers after a flood. Or was a shoal killed off by disease?

# LANG'S BEDS

A visit to the Graveyard of Ammonites might be considered a pilgrimage, second only to paying homage at the grave of Mary Anning. This woman is an outstanding figure in history of palaeontology but she lived during a period when the origins of fossils were hardly understood. Today we take it for granted that the Jurassic fossils we pick up around Lyme Regis are derived from creatures that lived about 200 millions of years ago, but you would have been hard pushed to convince anyone of this during the nineteenth century. An intriguing insight into the heated debates that preceded our understanding of the Jurassic Period can be had by reading "Dinosaur Hunters" by Deborah Cadbury. It was published in the year 2000 by Fourth Estate and later dramatised for Channel Four Television.

Armchair reading and TV viewing aside, **William Dickson Lang** is the name to remember if you intend to start a serious study of the fossil make-up of the cliffs around Lyme Regis. W.D.Lang made, literally, an inch-by-inch survey of the Lower Lias. His painstaking research has never been surpassed and is the framework upon which modern studies concerning the evolution of life in early Jurassic seas is based. His papers were published during the first half of the 20th century and they included beautifully illustrated maps of the ledges around Lyme Regis. Subsequently, "Lang's Beds" have become part of the jargon used by experienced fossil hunters in describing the location of their finds and by scientists when writing up their research. The Graveyard of Ammonites is Bed 29 of Lang's notation.

Along Monmouth Beach at low tide you can still see the mangled remnants of a railway built during the middle of the nineteenth century. It was used for hauling limestone to a cement factory which occupied much of the land to the west of the Cobb. The quarrymen's name for The Graveyard of Ammonites was Top Tape. Higher up in the cliffs is a band of limestone they called Best Bed, but most of the names they used (for example Upper and Lower Skulls, Mongrel and Gumption) appear to have no practical significance and await the attention of a diligent historian. Such a scholar will find Lang's paper on the Blue Lias very useful because it includes all the names used by the quarrymen and tips on how to identify each ledge. (The paper was published in 1924 in The Proceedings of the Geological Association, volume 35, pages 169-185, with a map).

A tough bed of limestone known to the quarrymen as Glass Bottle (Lang's Bed 47) often sticks out near to the top the Blue Lias. Its underside is usually full of huge specimens of *Arietites bucklandi*. The generic name (*Arietites*) of this ammonite is derived from the Latin for a ram and the origin of its specific name goes back to a time when geologists explored the country on horseback. During one of these forays around Bath the coil of a large ammonite was carried around the shoulders of the Reverend William Buckland in the manner of a french horn. His companions dubbed him the "Ammon Knight" and named the fossil after this "meritorious and enlightened geologist". This choice little anecdote was recalled by Thomas Wright in his superbly illustrated "Monograph on the Lias Ammonites of the British Islands" published by the Palaeontological Society in 1878.

# ZONE AMMONITES

Ammonites evolved into a great variety of species which came and went, some of which are used for dating the relative ages of the sediments in which they were laid down. The first in the sequence of *"zone ammonites"* used for Jurassic sediments (*Psiloceras planorbis*) need not concern us because the base of the Blue Lias lies well beneath Monmouth Beach. The earliest zone ammonite you might encounter is *Schlotheimia angulata*. This distinctive species is by no means common because the top of its range crops up above sea-level only along a limited stretch of the beach where the Blue Lias arches up. The shell of the ammonite is decorated with ribs that skirt the rim of the shell in the manner of a herringbone or the treads of a tyre. Loose body chambers derived from shale are unmistakable from this pattern alone. The suture lines occasionally show up on limestone. They are extremely complicated, resembling the outlines of feathers or ferns for which they are sometimes mistaken.

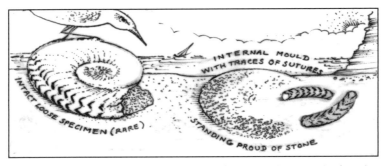

"Herringbone ammonites" – species of *Schlotheimia* named after the German palaeontologist Ernst von Schlotheim who promoted the use of fossils in working out the relative ages of ancient sediments .

*Schlotheimia angulata* and its relatives give way to the giant ammonites which range from the base of Monmouth beach towards the top of the Blue Lias. This range encompasses the Bucklandi Zone, named after the ammonite *Arietites bucklandi*. The next zone ammonite is a species of Arnie (*Arnioceras semicostatum*) which puts in an appearance at the top of the Blue Lias and extends into the lower part of the of the Shales-with-Beef.

You will find a list of the all the Jurassic zone ammonites in the book "British Mesozoic Fossils" published by The British Museum of Natural History. This standard work bridges the gap between the amateur and professional palaeontologist. It contains first-class line drawings of many of the Jurassic and Cretaceous fossils to be found around Lyme Regis. It has stood the test of time.

The identification of Zone Ammonites tells us nothing of course about the actual ages of the sediments in which they are buried and concerning which laboratory techniques are used which are beyond the scope of this booklet and the pocket of the amateur. These techniques are based upon the rates of radioactive decay of substances within the sediments. Such methods are being refined all the time making textbooks and other publications rapidly out of date. For this reason your author has resisted the temptation to assign specific dates to the fossils of Lyme Regis.

# NAUTILOIDS

Slabs of Blue Lias containing the impressions of large shells of nautiloids.

The impressions of large nautiloid shells are common in the boulders of Monmouth Beach but they are easily mistaken for those of ammonites. In contrast to most ammonites the walls that separate the air chambers of nautiloids are beautifully curved like the blades of a turbine engine. The outer coil of the nautiloid shell overlaps most of the inner ones giving rise to an impression not unlike a tight dumbbell when the shell is exposed across its middle. However, the principal feature that distinguishes a nautiloid from an ammonite is the manner in which a thread of tissue resembling a bootlace ran through the air chambers. This tissue was almost certainly involved in regulating the amount of air within the shell. It was enclosed in a shelly tube known as a **siphucle**. In the ammonite the siphuncle was closely applied to the periphery the shell (running through the keel if it had one) whereas in the nautiloid it pierced the centre of each septum. It will be evident that a complete sequence of these apertures will show up in a nautiloid only if the shell is exposed exactly across the middle of its flat axis (as in the illustration above).

Ammonites disappeared with the dinosaurs but nautiloids are still with us though restricted to a handful of species living in the Indo-Pacific ocean. These "living fossils" are of immense interest because of the light they may throw upon the lifestyle and appearance of their extinct relatives. The skin of the best known surviving nautiloid is patterned maroon and yellow and its cleaned-up shell is of a beautiful pearly hue from which the creature gets its common name, The Pearly Nautilus. No doubt many extinct nautiloids and ammonites likewise sported a fine livery before they were entombed in the mud which now makes up the grey rocks around Lyme Regis. The shell of the commonest species of Jurassic nautiloid found on Monmouth Beach is decorated with striations that run parallel to its curvature.

# BELEMNITES

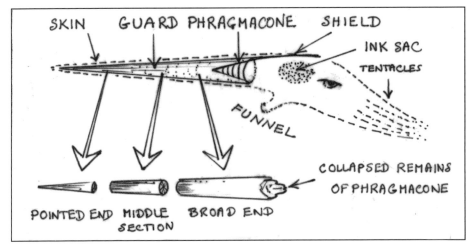

The structure of the belemnite and its fossilizised parts that are commonly found on the beaches to the east of Lyme Regis. Its fleshy parts (conjectural) are indicated by dashed lines. The siphon was a flexible tube that squeezed out water enabling the creature to move about by "jet propulsion". This organ of locomotion was common to all its relatives including the extinct ammonites and the squids and octopuses of today.

The impressions of the soft parts of belemnites are extremely rare and when we say that we have found a belemnite it is always understood that we have only picked up its **guard**. This is a bullet-shaped mass of calcite that occupied the rear end of the creature. The calcite was built up in concentric layers and this gives rise to a pattern not unlike the growth rings of a tree when a freshly broken guard is viewed end-on. This feature together with its smooth and streamlined surface makes an unworn guard easy to tell apart from any other object on the beach.

Guards are tough but brittle and loose specimens derived from shale are invariably broken up into fragments as they are washed out of the cliffs. These pieces can be categorised as follows: a pointed end, a middle section (or sections), and a squashed end into which fitted a cone divided into air chambers by vertical partitions of calcite. This cone (or **phragmocone,** to give its proper name) is equivalent to the chambered shell of an ammonite. The guard can be viewed as an extension of the light phragmacone about which it acted as a counterweight.

The upper surface of the phragmacone was extended forwards as a protective shield above the head of the animal. This shield is occasionally preserved in broad outline on limestone or tough shale, but otherwise the only other part of a belemnite that you are likely to find is a dark splodge where there was once an ink sac. The ink was squirted out by the belemnite as a smoke screen to confuse its enemies. Its living relatives (squids and cuttlefish) still do so. The ink itself was actually used for writing letters by a friend of Mary Anning. Samples of this fascinating correspondence are on display at the Philpot Museum of Lyme Regis.

It is instructive to compare the guards of belemnites with cuttlefish "bones". These are the white and brittle slipper-shaped objects that are often found on the beaches around Lyme Regis. They are much sought after as a rich supply of calcium for budgies and canaries.

Each cuttlefish "bone" is really a shell. It occupied most of the broad back of the living animal. An intact shell will have a needle-like point at one end. This is homologous to the belemnite guard. The rest of the shell is a flattened phragmacone containing a great number of compressed walls. The cavities between the walls are filled with air and this is the reason why cuttlefish bones float and why they are washed up on the seashore. The phragmacones of Jurassic cuttlefish occasionally show up in the rocks of Lyme Regis.

In the octopus and squid all that is left of a shell is a thin and transparent structure homologous to the shield of the belemnite. Consequently, the evolution of these extraordinary creatures has scarcely left a trace in the fossil record.

Belemnites certainly evolved into innumerable species but all we have to go on are details of the guard, such as its shape (variations on the bullet theme) and the relative size of the phragmacone. Important work on the classification of belemnites was carried out by W.D. Lang who discovered several new species. He named them after saints as most of them were found around Saint Gabriel's Mouth to the east of Charmouth.

Belemnites have been known as "Devil's Darts" and "Thunderbolts". Locally, they were once called Cromwell's Bullets. That was around 1644 when the town was under siege by Royalist troops during the English Civil War. They appear to have been put to good use as weapons within living memory; several senior citizens of Lyme Regis have told me that as boys they waged war against each other using arrows of bamboo tipped with belemnites!

Some forty years after the siege of Lyme Regis many of its inhabitants went to war again. The Duke of Monmouth landed on the beach we are exploring on the 11th of June 1685. He had every intention in taking the crown form his uncle King James the Second but he was defeated at the battle of Sedgemoor in Somerset. The notorious Judge Jeffries taught the rebels a lesson, hanging a dozen of them on the spot where Monmouth had disembarked. Ever since then the beach has been named after the hapless Duke.

Belemnites are exceptionally common in the sediment named after them –The Belemnite Marls. This is not present in the cliffs of Monmouth Beach but it forms a major component of the cliffs on other the side of Lyme Regis. Consequently, belemnites are relatively uncommon on Monmouth Beach.

# BIVALVED MOLLUSCS

The shellfish that we have considered make up part of the hierarchy of the great animal kingdom which we call molluscs. Today this hierarchy (known as the Cephalapoda, meaning head-footed) is poorly represented but very well known, consisting of octopuses, squids, cuttlefish and the like. The molluscs that have stood the test of time are those that were early adapted to a sedentary life on the sea-bed, These are the "ordinary shellfish" of today – bivalved molluscs – equipped with two shells which enclose and protect their fleshy parts: oysters, mussels, cockles and their kin. Common Jurassic species found on Monmouth Beach are pictured below.

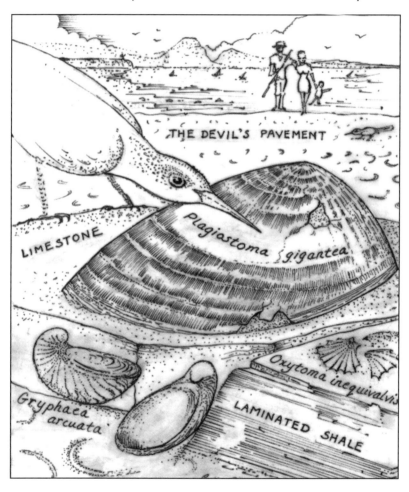

Bivalve molluscs are somewhat conservative in evolutionary terms. The shell of a Jurassic scollop, for example, is similar to that of a scollop dredged up today from the bottom of Lyme Bay. In contrast, the shells of ammonites evolved into a great variety of forms throughout the Jurassic period as if they were experimenting in ways to escape and hide from the reptiles that hunted them.

The best known Jurassic bivalve is an oyster popularly known as the **"Devil's Toenail"** or Gryph (pronounced "griff") after its Latin name *Gryphaea arcuata*. This species flourished over an enormous period and its remains are very common in the Blue Lias. It is a splendid example of how fossils can provide a clue to conditions on ancient sea-floors in so far as many of the oysters of today thrive in muddy seas.

The lower shell of the Gryph is a tough cup upon which rested the upper flat and lid-like shell. The two shells were linked together at their narrow ends by ligaments which quickly rotted away after death – complete Gryphs are uncommon. The lower shell is twisted upwards at one end. It is decorated with concentric and overlapping ridges representing phases of growth. This ornamentation is soon lost when the shell is tossed about on the beach but the shell is still easy to recognise from its domed and slipper-like appearance.

Those shells which are buried in limestone and which have been worn across show up as crescent-shaped impressions that resemble toe clippings. These impressions are exceptionally common on the surface of the first layer of limestone above The Graveyard of Ammonites. This **"Devil's Pavement"**, as we might call it, was known to the quarrymen as Third Quick. It was named Bed 30 by W.D.Lang.

The only shell-fish that might be mistaken for the Jurassic Gryph is the Cretaceous oyster known as **Exogyra**. It is common in Greensand and frequently turns up on the beaches around Lyme Regis. Both these shell-fish are typically of the same size but whereas the twisted portion of the lower shell is raised up in the Gryph, it curls around the plane of the shell in *Exogyra*.

The largest Jurassic bivalve to be found on the beaches around Lyme Regis is **Plagiostoma gigantica.** Its shell can be as big as a cereal bowl, but it is very thin and is rapidly worn down leaving only the pudding-shaped lump of limestone it encapsulated. When freshly exposed its glistening black shell attracts immediate attention, however. Details of its decoration are then perfectly preserved and consist of very fine growth rings crossed by a pattern of radiating lines emanating from the narrow end of the shell. It follows that the finest specimens of this shell-fish are only revealed in freshly broken limestone. Such a fracture can occur naturally but otherwise you will need a chisel and a great deal of patience to do justice to *Plagoiostoma*.

Another thin and finely decorated Jurassic shellfish is a type of scollop known as **Oxytoma**. Its shells are common in shale but they are usually compressed. The characteristic features of the scollop family are flat extensions on either side of the hinged margins of the shells. Although these "ears" were very pronounced in *Oxytoma* they are usually flattened beyond recognition in the shale.

In addition to bivalved molluscs, fossilized marine snails (members of the moluscan kingdom known as gastropods) derived from the Blue Lias sometimes show up on Monmouth Beach but they are too rare to warrant description here.

Incidently, the lady of the tongue-twister "She sells seashells on the sea-shore" is said to have been Mary Anning.

# BRACHIOPODS

The molluscan bivalve lies on its side as if it were in bed with the lower shell for a mattress and the upper one for a blanket. The brachiopod has two shells but this creature lies on its belly with one shell protecting its underparts and the other covering its back. Moreover, the soft parts of the mollusc differ from those of the brachiopod.

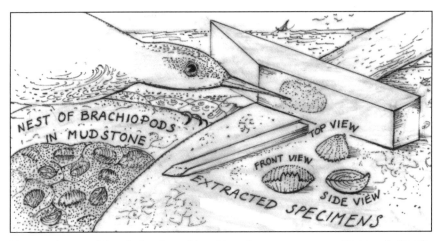

Fine specimens of the shells of small brachiopods are common on Monmouth Beach and are easy to extract from hardened shale ("mudstone").

The commonest type of brachiopod within the Blue Lias (**_Calcirhynchia calcaria_**) is no bigger than the tip of your little finger and is easily mistaken for a tiny cockle. The fossils are usually covered with a veneer of silvery calcite and feel waxy. An exquisite feature is the way in which the broad ends of the shells meet to form a crenulated edge puckered up in the middle like a hood. When viewed sideways the lower shell is seen to turn up at its narrow end in the manner of an Aladdin's lamp. The lower shells of much larger modern brachiopods were used as oil lamps from at least the time of the Romans and this use has given rise to the popular name for brachiopods: **lamp shells**. The largest brachiopod that turns up on Monmouth Beach (_Spiriferina walcotti_) is about the size of a walnut but it is far from common.

The tiny Jurassic specimens are best appreciated under your hand lens. Look for traces of a tiny hole on the upturned end of the lower shell. Out of this hole sprouted threads of tissue in the form of a miniature rope which anchored the brachiopod to the seabed. The hole is normally filled up with hard sediment but its outline is often apparent. You will sometimes come across colonies ("nests") of brachiopods buried in tough shale (mudstone) and from which perfect specimens can be extracted with little effort. Clusters of _Calcirhynchia_ that have been worn across often show up on the surfaces of limestone. The cavities of the shells are then exposed and almost invariably they are lined by calcite crystals.

If you get hooked on brachiopods then you should read up on _Lingula_, the most famous brachiopod of all time. It goes back 500 millions of years and is still with us. This famous "living fossil" is described in every standard textbook of zoology.

# CRINOIDS

The Jurassic sea-floor was certainly rich in seaweeds but the soft tissues of these plants are scarcely represented in the rocks around Lyme Regis. In contrast, creatures popularly known as "sea-lilies" were sfiffened with plates of calcium carbonate and are common as fossils. Their scientific name – crinoids – was derived from the greek word for lily. That was long before before it was realized that they were not plants but stalked relatives of starfish.

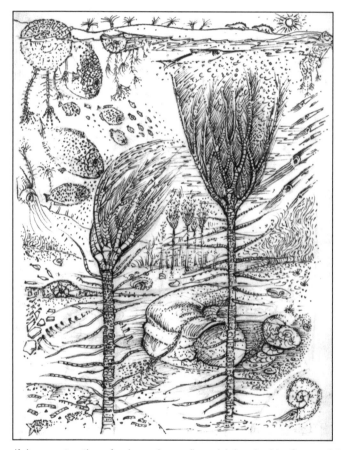

A fanciful reconstruction of a Jurassic sea floor rich in crinoids. Some of these creatures are shown dangling from driftwood in keeping with their common association as fossilized remains on the beaches around Lyme Regis.

The stalk was ringed at intervals by whip-like projections. It was surmounted by a kind of knuckle which contained the vital organs and around which arose five branching arms which formed an intricate web. On the top of the knuckle was a mouth into which microscopic food particles were channelled by the movements of hair-like projections that lined the inner surface of the web. The stalks and appendages were made up of star-shaped units held together by ligaments.

Many of the limestone boulders on Monmouth beach are splattered with the disintegrated remains of crinoids. They show up as star-shaped impressions wherever the stalk has been worn across and as ladder-like segments reminiscent of bits of tapeworms wherever the stalk has been eroded along its length. These fragments often adorn the impressions of large ammonites and nautilods indicating that the shells provided useful anchoring points for crinoids. Loose pieces of stalk derived from shale are not uncommon but they are rarely thicker than a pencil and it takes a sharp eye to find them. When viewed end-on under a lens the surface of an unworn stalk is seen to be decorated with a beautiful pattern resembling the petals of a flower. The details of this pattern are useful in telling crinoids apart. The commonest species found around Lyme Regis is **Pentacrinites fossilis**.

The most sought after specimens of crinoids are thin plates of crystalline limestone made up of their matted remains after they had flopped over on the sea-bed. Known as **crinoid plates**, these exquisite splinters of Jurassic history are far from common on Monmouth Beach. The best specimens are derived from a thin pavement no more than a centimeter thick and known as the **Pentacrinite Bed** which is situated in the middle of the Black Ven Marls. The base of these Marls is present high up on the cliffs of Monmouth Beach but its full thickness starts on the other side of Lyme Regis where crinoid plates first put in a significant appearance on the beaches.

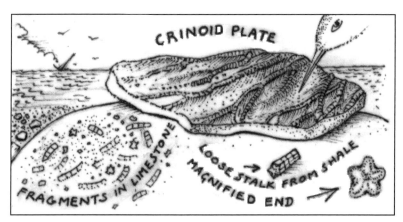

Fossilized remains of crinoids. Sometimes a crinoid plate is made up of pyrites in which details of the fossils are beautifully preserved.

Fossilized driftwood is commonly found on one of the surfaces of a crinoid plate indicating that the creatures were attached to it in the manner of dangling goose barnacles. A curious feature of *Pentacrinities* is the lack of any sort of root in contrast to many other types of crinoid.

Crinoids are extremely ancient. They carpeted sea-floors long before the Jurassic Period. It is not unliklely that an offshoot of the crinoid stock lost its stalk and that its five-fingered head effectively turned over and crawled on the seabed, giving rise to starfishes. Crinoids are still with us today but they are mostly represented as stalkless swimming creatures known as feather stars.

# JURASSIC FISH

Fish are essentially of two sorts: those with a skeleton of cartilage and those with a skeleton of bone. The cartilaginous fish are mostly made up of sharks and rays.

**Sharks** were common in Jurassic seas but cartilage rots away quickly and only the very hard parts of these fish have survived as fossils, notably their enamelled teeth. These are occasionally found loose on the seashore where they been washed out of shale. Typical specimens are black and shiny with a delightful surface decoration of fine ridges and grooves.

In some species of ancient sharks the leading edge of each fin on the back was supported by a hard spine. Fossilized bits of this spine sometimes turn up on the beaches but complete specimens are rare. The spine is somewhat flat in cross-section and its surface is thrown into folds. Because of these features, pieces of the spine are sometimes mistaken for bark derived from driftwood. A curious feature of the spine is a row of hook-like projections emanating from its hind edge. Details such as these are used in determining "new" species.

The best known Jurassic shark is **Hybodus**. A reconstruction of this fish is illustrated below together with its fossilized remains that sometimes show up on the beaches around Lyme Regis.

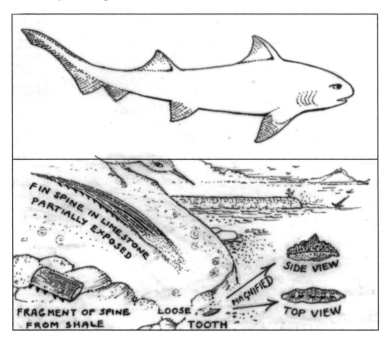

FIN SPINE PARTIALLY IN LIMESTONE EXPOSED

FRAGMENT OF SPINE FROM SHALE

LOOSE TOOTH

MAGNIFIED

SIDE VIEW

TOP VIEW

The typical bony fish of today are noted for their great variety of form and number of species (twenty thousand at least). They had hardly got going during the Jurassic Period when their ancestors were a mere offshoot of the bony fish which then dominated the seas. These ancient fish are known as **holosteans** of which only two groups are represented today (the bowfins and garpikes).

In contrast to modern bony fish, holosteans are noted for their thick enamelled scales. Isolated scales of holosteans are common in Jurassic shale but are easily overlooked. They show up as glistening black or brown specs often no larger, and somewhat resembling, fleas. A patch of holostean scales resembles a piece of snake's skin and is worth keeping. A fin is a prize and complete fish a trophy.

Especially sought after are specimens of the deep bodied holostean **Dapedium** preserved in saucer-shaped plates of limestone and in which the fish forms a natural cleavage plane enabling the rock to split in half (with luck!) when tapped edge-on with a hammer. This famous Jurassic fish gets its name from the latin word for pavement; its scales fit together like a Roman mozaic. Its head is covered in grey plates studded with black pimples and Its needle-like teeth are grouped together in small mouth. Perhaps the fish had similar habits to the nibbling piranha of today.

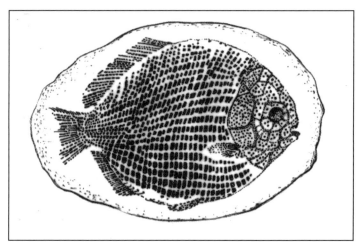

*Dapedium,* exposed in a slab of Blue lias found on Monmouth B each and viewed from above. The fish formed a natural cleavage plane. When the slab was viewed edge-on the fish showed up only as a thin band of chequered markings.

The only other Jurassic fish that is at all common is the holostean **Pholidophorus.** It was more streamlined than *Dapedium* and looked something like the herring of today. Its fossilized scales are brown rather than black.

Remains of one the world's most famous "living fossil" – the **coelocanth** – have been found around Lyme Regis. This fish appeared long before holosteans evolved and well before the Jurassic Period. Until a specimen was dredged up in the 1930's off the coast of South Africa everyone thought it had become extinct by the end of the Cretaceous Period.

# MARINE REPTILES

Every fossil hunter exploring the beaches around Lyme Regis would love to find the complete skeleton of a Jurassic marine reptile. After all, the cliffs around Lyme Regis are the source of the best preserved remains of these creatures to be found anywhere in the world, and new species are often brought to light as the cliffs erode. The good news is that many skeletons of these extinct creatures are buried in the cliffs, poised as it were to make spectacular landings on the seashore in the wake of cliff falls and mud flows. The bad news is that most of these remains lie flat and twisted just as the entire animals did as they rotted on the sea floor. When exposed in a vertical cliff face the bones show up as nothing more than a curious sequence of dark markings where they have been cut through, as in the remains of fish.

*These impressions are difficult to recognize let alone decipher without a lot of experience and a fair knowledge of vertebrate anatomy. Moreover, going close enough to the cliffs to seek them out is fraught with danger and extracting a skeleton covered over with tons of sediment is out of the question.*

But the skeletal remains of reptiles are continually brought down to the seashore as the cliffs erode and although anything approaching a complete skeleton is exceptional, every fossil hunter has a good chance of finding a loose bone. Skeletons derived from soft shale are rapidly broken up and dispersed by wave action and only the tougher parts survive for any length of time.

The commonest bone found on the beach, or rather the easiest to recognize, is the solid base of a **vertebra** derived from an ichthyosaur. It is shaped like a round pillbox with the lid and bottom pushed in and it is known as the **centrum.** It will be evident from this description that when cut across its middle, a centrum will look like a bow-tie or an hour-glass, as depicted during our discussion on body chamber ammonites. The projections on the sides of the centrum for the attachment of the ribs can usually be made out in loose and unworn specimens. The centrum was surmounted by a bony arch through which ran the spinal cord. The top of this arch was extended upwards as a spine for the attachment of muscles. This part of the vertebra together with the ribs was soon detached and broken up.

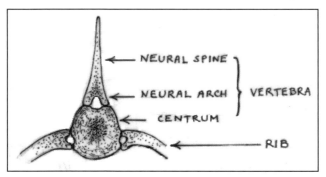

Cross-section of the bones that made up the back of an ichthyosaur. Only the tough centrum is normally found as a loose fossil. The positions of the projections on the centrum for the double-headed ribs vary according to which part of the back (including the neck and tail) the centrum was derived.

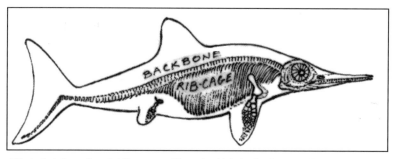

Simplified skeleton of an Ichthyosaur. Note the kink in the bones of the tail. Before soft impressions of the reptile were discovered these bones were straightened out as a continuation of the backbone when the skeleton was reconstructed. The ring of bony plates that supported the eye is highly characteristic but all parts of the skull apart from the tough rostrum are crushed almost beyond recognition in many fossilized skeletons.

The ichthyosaur had an enormous number of vertebrae and this is another reason why its centra are not uncommon as loose fossils. Its rib-cage was also made up of many bones but these rather brittle elements soon break up into pieces during their exit from the cliffs.

The toughest bits of reptiles (as in us) were their **teeth.** These withstand buffeting on the seashore extremely well and superb specimens sometimes show up. They are shaped like pegs and like those of Jurassic sharks are covered with glistening black enamel. In the reptile, the enamel is decorated by longitudinal ridges. The teeth of the ichthyosaur fitted into grooves (not sockets) along the jaw bones and were prone to dissemination as the skeleton disintegrated. If, however, the reptile died with its mouth shut then its interlocking teeth aided the preservation of the jaws as a unit. At any rate, parts of the **rostrum** or "beak" of an ichthyosaur with its jaws glued together are not all that rare. If you are lucky enough to find a piece then examine its ends. If they appear to be freshly broken then the rest of the rostrum could be lying about the beach.

Another part of the ichthyosaur skeleton that is sometimes found as a fossilized unit is the mosaic of bones that supported a flipper. This instrument of steering (sideway movements of the tail propelled the reptile) provides us with a major insight into the evolution of marine reptiles. All these creatures were derived from reptiles that lived on land. In taking to the sea, the limb bones were adapted to support flippers. The major bones of the forelimb (humerus, radius and ulna) have been reduced to tough stumps from which emanate the flattened wrist bones and fingers that form the bulk of the flipper. Differences in the detailed make-up of these bones are most important because they are one of the principal means of telling different species of ichthyosaurs apart.

Loose bones of plesiosaurs are harder to come by than those of ichthyosaurs. It may well be that plesiosaurs were less common than ichthyosaurs but differences between their skeletons should also be taken into account. Species of both types of reptile ranged in length from less than three to over thirty feet, but size-for-size the plesiosaur had fewer vertebrae and ribs. Futhermore, the plesiosaur was far less adapted to a maritime lifestyle than its diving cousin and lacked distinctive features

Fossilized parts of an Ichthyosaur skeleton derived from shale. The rostrum is a typical specimen in which the teeth have been fossilized askew and are partially buried in the bony matrix of the fused jaws, making them difficult to recognize at first sight.

that are easy to recognise, such a tough rostrum. It used its flippers like oars to move about on the surface of the sea and these appendages retained more of the pattern of its land-dwelling ancestors, notably the finger bones. These resembled bobbins and never joined up to form a flattened interlocking system favourable to fossilization as a disarticulated unit derived from shale. The paddles needed strong muscles to do their work, however, and a big bone found on the beach might well be part of the massive undercarriage to which these muscles were attached.

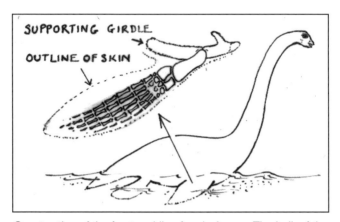

Construction of the front paddle of a plesiosaur. The bulk of the paddle is made up of bones homologous to those of your hand.

The centrum of a plesiosaur is thicker than that of an ichthyosaur and resembles a somewhat flattened cotton reel rather than a pillbox. Bits of rib derived from a plesiosaur are also distinctive. They are blade-like rather than circular in cross-section.

Fragments of bone often show up on the surfaces of limestone boulders derived from the Blue Lias, but they are easily passed over for Jurassic driftwood. This is where your hand lens really comes in useful. Fossilized bone has a distinctive appearance when magnified. Particularly evident are minute flecks of white calcite that have infiltrated the dark grey or black matrix of the bone tissue.

These specimens are usually isolated fragments derived from a skeleton that was broken up and widely scattered about the seabed after the carcass was torn apart by scavengers. But If you are lucky enough to find a stone splattered with black markings then it might contain something much more substantial, such as the remains of a crushed skull. Such a stone is too important to break open with a hammer and you are urged to take it to a local fossil shop for advice.

Bone is largely made up of calcium phosphate and this does not dissolve in acid as readily as the calcium carbonate of the limestone in which the bones are buried. By immersing the stone in acid and protecting the bones with varnish as they appear, the skull or otherwise is gradually brought to light. This technique requires great skill and access to dangerous chemicals. If the stone is worthy of this treatment then the shop will put you touch with a local expert who can do the job for you at a reasonable price.

We have no more room to consider in detail the fossilized remains of the extraordinary swimming reptiles for which Lyme Regis is world famous, and I leave you to peruse the splendid specimens on view in local fossil shops and the Philpot museum. Bear in mind that the skeletons took months if not years to prepare and that they were never easy to find.

If it suits your itinerary then be sure to visit Dorset County Museum in Dorchester. As you might expect it contains a very comprehensive collection of fossils that were found all along the Jurassic Coast.

If you live in London then you will have immediate access to the best collection of marine reptiles in the world. It is housed in the British Museum of Natural History together with a contemporary oil painting of Mary Anning and some of the reptilian skeletons she collected around Lyme Regis. These specimens were some of many that set up a stream of interest during the first half of the nineteenth century, culminating perhaps, in your very own visit to the coast she explored,

Before resuming our search for commoner fossils we should consider another type of reptile that, in the history of English palaentology, will always be associated with Mary Anning. A reptile with wings.

# FLYING REPTILES

The bones of flying reptiles (pterosaurs) were mostly hollow as an adaptation for flight and quickly disintegrated after death. The few remains that have been found around Lyme Regis are the most treasured of all its fossils and although the chances of finding any are remote, every fossil hunter should have a working knowledge of the skeletal framework of the pterosaur just in case it shows up.

The skeleton of *Dimporhodon* and a reconstruction of the living reptile

In all pterosaurs the parchment-like wing was supported by an enormous elongation of the fourth finger. Other fingers poked out in front of the leading edge of the wing and were tipped by claws. The feet of pterosaurs were very short in relation to the wingspan and these creatures must have looked very clumsy if they tried to walk. They are often pictured hanging upside down by the claws of their feet from the branch of a tree or a cliff ledge. Perhaps they roosted like today's bats. At any rate, anything resembling a claw is worthy of the attention of the fossil hunter if only because this tough appendage, like a tooth, needed to be strong and stood a fair chance of fossilization.

The first complete skeleton of a flying reptile ever recorded in England was discovered in cliffs around Lyme Regis by Mary Anning in 1828. It was named **Dimorphodon** after its two kinds of teeth (*di;* two: *don;* tooth). *Dimorphodon* is the earliest known type of Jurassic pterosaur and it appears to have been a fish-eater. Its teeth projected forwards and its gaping jaw would have made an excellent sieve for scooping up fish swimming at the surface of the sea. We might envisage some of these creatures getting stuck in mud as they fished in shallow and turbulent seas. This might have been the fate of Anning's specimen, but perhaps this creature was an exhausted individual that floated down to the seabed where it became trapped in sediment under quieter conditions.

*Dimorphodon* had a wingspan not much greater than a big gull and the majority of Jurassic pterosuars were rather small, many of them no larger than a rock pipit. The giant pterosuars such as the famous *Pteranodon* with a twenty foot wing-span and a huge anvil-shaped head did not appear until well into the Cretaceous Period. Pterosaurs are of two types. The more primitive type had teeth and a rather long tail which was often tipped by a diamond-shaped "rudder". The rudderless *Dimorphodon* belongs to this group. The more advanced pterosaurs (the pterodactyls) of which *Pteranodon* was a member had few if any teeth (reducing the weight of the body as an adaptation for flight) and the tail was short.

# PINHAY BAY AND COASTAL EROSION

When you reach the headland known as Seven Rock Point you will be tempted to go beyond it and explore Pinhay Bay. At the time of writing the headland is crumbling fast, bringing down trees from the clifftops.

*Even if the tide is well out and the cliffs look stable then bear in mind that as soon as you go beyond Seven Rock Point you will be out of sight of the town.*

Furthermore, the beaches of PInhay Bay are strewn with big boulders making it tough going and unsuitable for families.

The best views of the geological features that make up the Jurassic Coast are to be had by boat and the reader can take advantage of the several pleasure trips available from the Cobb during the warmer months of the year. He would then see the magnificent rise of the the Blue lias in the cliffs of Pinhay Bay where its full thickness of about 100 feet is exposed and beneath which the White Lias puts in an appearance. This is a cream coloured rock rich in crushed molluscan bivalves but without a single ammonite. It is believed to have been laid down as sediments in land-locked basins while ammonites were evolving elsewhere. Eventually the basins were flooded with seas teeming with ammonites many of which were subsequently buried in the sediments that now make up the Blue Lias.

*Going beyond Pinhay Bay without local knowledge is asking for trouble. For at least five miles there are several headlands where you can be cut of by the tides and there is no obvious escape route up the cliffs.*

*Moreover, even if you were able to scale the cliffs you would find yourself in a dense woodland akin to jungle,concealing dangerous crevices.*

The coastal strip between Lyme Regis and Axmouth has been left alone since 1839 when a gigantic landslip roused national panic, appeased only by Mary Anning's learned contemporaries who assured the Government that southern England was not about to disappear under an earthquake. Meanwhile the cliff-top from Lyme Regis to Axmouth has developed into a magnificent woodland mostly made up of ash trees and making it one of the wildest stretches of coastland in England.

You are therefore advised to head back to town after reaching Seven Rock point especially if you have children with you. You will have become familiar with tide conditions and this will put you in good stead for exploring the beaches on the other side of Lyme Regis where the sea is especially notorious for trapping the unwary visitor.

If you are a teacher leading a company of youngsters then this is the time to bring up the subject of coastal erosion if only because it is included in the English National Curriculum.

As you make your way back to the Cobb it will become evident from the structure of the cliffs that the tough blue Lias dips beneath Lyme Regis bringing down the much softer Shales-with-Beef and Black Ven Marls upon which the town is built. You will have seen the manner in which the formations overlying the Blue Lias continually slip down all the way along Monmouth beach. How then, has the town survived?

For centuries the natural flow of shingle from west to east was unimpeded. There was always a gap between the Cobb and the seashore. The shingle was trapped by a complex system of groynes that jutted out along the sea front. It was this shingle that protected the base of town from the action of the waves. At the same time the flow of shingle helped to scour out the harbour.

In 1756 the gap between the Cobb and the land was filled in, but not high enough to stop the flow of shingle at low tide. It was only during living memory that this bridge was developed in such a way that free flow of shingle was stopped. Ever since then the shingle has piled up against the Cobb. During stormy weather it is flung over into the harbour, sometimes damaging boats.

Meanwhile the harbour has become silted up and it now encloses something of puddle compared with the deep water that it once contained and which was essential for the tall ships that used to offload their cargo on the Cobb. A sand-bar to the north of the harbour has built up much to the delight of the holiday maker and the tourist trade while the base of the sea-front has been subjected to the full mercy of sea, resulting in something of nightmare for local authorities.

In 1962 a massive landslip above the seafront brought a house down in its wake following the grubbing up of land by a property developer. Subsequently, the gardens were laid out as you see them today. The eastern end of the gardens slipped in a big way in 1994, settling above a walkway that is now cordoned off. Since then the frontage around the mouth of the River Lym has been protected by the development of a multimillion pound sea defence system which included massive boulders that now do the work that was once done by shingle.

Not that the fossil hunter is grumbling! After stormy weather the shingle beneath the Bay Hotel (midway along the seafront) is sometimes completely cleared away revealing one of the topmost layers of the Blue lias which is full of giant ammonites and nautilods. If you are lucky enough to see them then immediately snap away with your camera; plans are afoot to restore a permanent shingle bank all the way along the seafront. Everyone living in Lyme Regis hopes that should this next multimillion project get underway then it will be successful in protecting the town. But it is a sobering thought that the magnificent fossils that are sometimes exposed at the foot of the town will have only seen the light of day during a brief period in the history of Lyme Regis.

# THE EASTERN BEACHES

A short walk from the foot of the town and along the walls of the eastern sea defence system will bring you face to face with a curving beach extending from Lyme Regis to Charmouth. This beach skirts the foot of Black Ven, the site of a gigantic landslip out of which some of the world's finest Jurassic fossils have come to light.

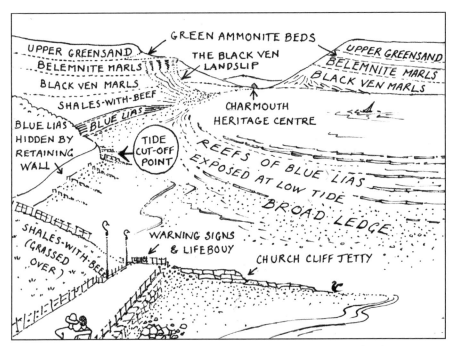

Rough sketch (not to scale) of coastal features to the east of Lyme Regis. The Gault is hidden by falls of Upper Greensand and the wedge of Green Ammonite Beds above the Ven is difficult to make out from a distance. *Note the tide cut-off point. Broad Ledge is the last of the reefs to be covered over as the tide comes in, making it a useful "marker". See text for details.*

A walk along the beaches from Lyme Regis towards Black Ven and back can be delightful at low tide. For much of the way you will be walking over sand. The cliff formations are magnificent and you will share the beaches with rock pipits, oystercatchers, and other interesting shore-birds.

*But before setting out it is imperative to check tide conditions. As indicated in the sketch you can be cut off by the tide at a bend in the cliffs on your way back. Bear in mind when looking up tide-tables that you have to add an hour on during the summer in keeping with British Summer Time. You should also take into account the direction of the wind. If it is blowing from the south then the tide can come in quicker than predicted.*

*If you are unfamiliar with the area then you are strongly advised not to go beyond the cut-off point unless the tide is going out with you and to head back to town as soon as the tide starts to turn.* The itinerary which follows has been drawn up with this factor in mind. and assumes that you have chosen an outgoing tide sufficiently low to expose expansive reefs of limestone.

These reefs are made up of layers of Blue Lias which are continuous with those which form the base of the cliffs. The Jurassic formations that once lay above them have been scoured away by modern seas. Not quite so obvious is the way in which the reefs buckle up like the squashed rings of an onion skin and about which the sea has cut into the shale, giving rise to a system of shallow rock pools. Cleared of encrustations and viewed from above, these reefs would tell us much about life on Jurassic sea-floors. No one is going to strip off all the remarkable animals and plants that live on this designated Site of Special Scientific Interest, but there is always a chance of finding a loose centrum or other interesting fossils derived from eroded shale and trapped within a rock pool.

As you make your way down to the beach you will pass through space once occupied by part of the graveyard of Saint Michael's Church where Mary Anning is buried. The retaining wall was built in 1910 following a public outcry after human skeletons were seen poking out of the cliffs. The wall was extended in the direction of Charmouth, obscuring the rise of the Blue Lias after its dip beneath the town. This is unfortunate from the fossil hunting point of view because the wall hides the top part of the Blue Lias which contains the saurian and fish beds named after their profusion of vertebrate remains. But there is much to observe on the seashore between the groynes that project from the walls. Where clear of shingle you should be able to make out patches of those highly fossiliferous layers of limestone that we saw on the other side of town: "The Graveyard of Ammonites" and "The Devil's Pavement".

The wall ends just after the last groyne, beyond which the cliffs immediately curve inwards where they are partly protected by a heap of granite boulders that was dragged to the site in 1999. From this point onwards the Blue Lias is exposed as a sheer cliff face similar to that of Monmouth Beach.

*You will be tempted to rummage at the base of the cliffs for fossils but this is extremely dangerous. Moreover, boulders derived from exactly the same formation are far more plentiful on Monmouth Beach where, as we have seen, they can be examined in safety well away from the cliffs.*

You are advised, then, to keep going until the top of the Blue Lias descends to the beach. From then onwards mudlows are frequent bringing with them fossils derived from the formations which overlie the Blue Lias. The mud spreads over the beaches where it is rapidly dispersed by wave action, leaving the heavier fossils trapped within belts of shingle. Many of these fossils are derived from the Shales-with-Beef which is brought down to sea-level in the wake of the Blue Lias. The guards of belemnites also become common. Most of them originate from the Belemnite Marls, a formation which is absent in the cliffs of Monmouth beach but very evident high up in the Ven where it puts in its first appearance along the Jurassic Coast. The guards are rarely thicker than your little finger and you will need to carefully scour the beach to find them. This is also the first place where fossils and minerals derived from the Black Ven Marls become significant; although the base of this formation is present in the cliffs of Monmouth Beach its full thickness starts in the Ven.

The Black Ven Marls is renowned for fine specimens of "fool's gold" (iron pyrites) and ammonites made up entirely of this attractive mineral. Pure "fool's gold" sparkles in the sunshine and when examined under a lens its box-shaped crystals become evident. Less attractive specimens in which the crystals are difficult to make out are more common but these lumps often contain the impressions of crushed ammonites. A curious form of pyrite that often turns up looks exactly like a tiny mushroom. It is sometimes put down to a fossilized sponge but its exact origin remains something of mystery.

Pyritised specimens of the the coin-sized ammonite *Promicroceras planicosta* ("**Prom**" for short) are especially sought after. The outstanding feature of this ammonite is the way in which the ribs are slightly compressed where they skirt the rim of the shell. The suture lines are often in evidence but they are no thicker than hairs and you will almost certainly need your lens to make them out. There must be many families who cherish, if not wear, the "Prom" they found at Lyme Regis but have never put it to the lens and seen its "Jurassic hall mark"!

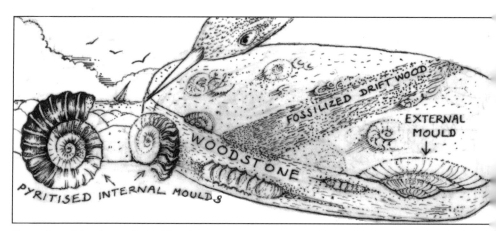

Examples of the internal moulds *of Promicroceras planicosta,* an ammonite known locally as a "Prom". An external mould of *Asteroceras obtusum* (a species of "Astie") is also illustrated. Note that the fossilized shell itself would be a thin cast, fragments of which often adhere to the external mould. Ammonites in Woodstone and its sister (Flatstone) give rise to natural cleavage planes which aid the extraction of the fossils. Note also the way in which the ribs of the Prom flatten out as they skirt the rim of the shell. In related species the ribs are extended as spines on either side of the shell. These armoured ammonites are called **"Ziffs"** by local fossil hunters, the only way to pronounce their proper name, *Xipheroceras*.

Pyritised Proms are much sought after as items for jewellry but they are subject to an annoying affliction that sometimes turns them to dust. This is nothing more than a chemical reaction that starts as soon as the pyrite is exposed to air, a process that can be curtailed if not eliminated, by coating the fossil with varnish after washing it thoroughly in fresh water and and leaving it to dry.

The fossil hunter experienced in the use of a geological hammer will be on the lookout for flat and oval-shaped pieces of light grey and finely grained limestone known as **Flatstones**. These often contain ammonites of a colour similar to that o milky coffee and with a surface as smooth as porcelain. The shells are brittle and are not easy to extract in one piece. They often pop out of the stone during such attempts. The cavitations left behind are the **external moulds** of the shells. Fragments of limestone containing them are frequently found in the wake of local collectors who scour the beaches for flatstones.

Ammonites of the porcelain type are also common in stones of a similar shape but of a greenish hue and of a somewhat fibrous texture. The stones usually contain fossilized wood and are known locally as **Woodstones**. Both types of stone are rich in Proms and they often contain ammonites of the genus *Asteroceras* – "**Asties**" for short. These are probably the most sought after of all the ammonites to be found around Lyme Regis if only because of their decorative value. They grew much larger than Proms and when partially exposed in a lump of limestone that has been honed beneath to fit a shelf they look wonderful. The suture lines are often very evident and the surfaces of the shells are usually shaded brown and orange due to variations in the concentration of iron impurities. Polished specimens lying about the seashore are liberally depicted on postcards and brochures, fooling the recipients into thinking that's the way they turn up on the beaches. They don't. It takes great skill to expose an Astie to full advantage and local knowledge in recognising the stone that contained it.

The shell of an Astie has a keel flanked by grooves and it is not unlike an Arnie derived from the Shales-with-Beef. But these features together with the ribs are not so well defined and the outer coil fattens up towards the opening of the shell in contrast to the Arnie in which the shell always resembles a neatly coiled rope.

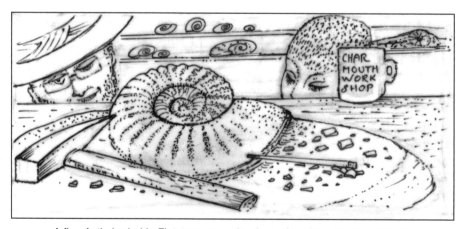

A fine Astie buried in Flatstone can take days of work to expose properly.

The flatstones and woodstones form impersistent bands in the lower half of the Black Ven Marls. In contrast, a row of nodules containing big Asties of the species *Asteroceras stellare* and known as the **Stellare Bed** is always present. This bed is situated very high up in the Ven and is not easy to make out from the seashore below. To the east of Charmouth, however, the Astie nodules can be seen poking out conspicuously from the cliffs as the Black Ven Marls descends to the beach beneath Stonebarrow Hill.

# THE BLACK VEN LANDSLIP

The Shales-with-B beef is far weaker than the Blue Lias. This goes some way in explaining the huge landslip which starts where the Blue Lias disappears beneath the beach and ends at Charmouth. Between these points the forces of coastal erosion have taken a spectacular bite out of the Jurassic Coast and have left behind a system of terraces which looks like a gigantic amphitheatre.

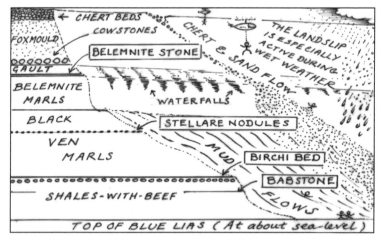

Schematic illustration of the western part of Black Ven with emphasis on fossil-rich layers and aspects of saftey. The Green Ammonite Beds puts its first appearance along the Jurassic Coast in the eastern part of the Ven, towards Charmouth.

In addition to a weak foundation, many other factors (mostly to do with water ensure the continual slippage of the Ven. Rainwater percolates rapidly through the capping of Greensand and is then impeded by the Gault clay and the Belemnite Stone, a pavement of hard limestone studded with belemnites. The water seeps out of the cliff-face giving rise to distinctive spidery markings. The saturated foxmould turns into a treacherous yellow soup akin to quicksand. This flows down to the beach bringing down chert rubble in its wake and pushing cowstones ahead. The tough and rather uniform Belemnite Marls tends to stay put, falling when it does in great chunks In contrast, the softer Black Ven Marls crumble rather than fall and its debris flatten out over its several layers of sturdy and often fossil-laden limestone.

*You might be tempted to climb this landslip in search of fossils, a foolhard exercise that sometimes results in a terrified visitor dangling from a helicopter as he is hauled off to hospital.* Moreover, because of the Jurassic tilt, all the formation above the Shales-with-Beef come down to sea-level on the other side of Charmouth where fossils derived from these formations are plentiful on the beaches.

*Fossil hunting is addictive and it is easy to forget the tide factor. Keep an eye on Broad Ledge – if it appears to be shrinking then you will know that the tide is coming in and that it is time to get back to town.* You will have gained a lot of experience that will put you in good stead for a visit to Charmouth which is only a few minutes drive from Lyme Regis.

# CHARMOUTH AND ITS DINOSAUR

The mouth of the river Char has a lot to offer the fossil hunter. The building close to the beach houses the Charmouth Heritage Centre which provides a splendid hands-on approach to fossils together with an audio-visual display that is guaranteed to wet the appetite of anyone new to fossil hunting. The walls of its snug auditorium are adorned with W.D. Lang's detailed maps of the Jurassic ledges around Lyme Regis and Charmouth. The remnants of a forest that clothed the valley of the Char many thousands of years ago, and which was drowned by the rise in sea level that followed the last ice age, are buried beneath the shingle which spans the river mouth. These remnants were exposed in a big way in 1924 when the shingle was cleared away during a storm and after which the antlers of red deer were collected by Lang. Further remains showed up in 2002.

Charmouth is renowned for a creature that lived on land during the Jurassic Period even though its cliffs are made up of maritime sediments. It is called *Scelidosaurus*. and it is the first known dinosuar that had plates on it back – an offshoot of the ancestral tree that led to the better known *Stegosaurus* which appeared long after the Jurassicsediments of the Lower Lias were laid down. Fossilized bones of *Scelidosaurus* were first recorded from the cliffs around Charmouth in 1851 and several more have turned up since together with impressions of its skin.

The Charmouth Dinosaur– as *Scelidosaurus* is known – must have been swept into the sea where it became buried in mud. Baby Skelidosaurs have been found and perhaps an entire herd of these creatures met a watery fate. If you have difficulty in remembering its name then think of a dinosaur skidding into the sea – "Skidosaurus" will do as a memory jog! It was a vegetarian and although your chances of finding its bones are slim its food source is common in the form of fossilized drift wood. The remains of the creature appear to be restricted to a seam in the Black Ven Marls.

A fanciful reconstruction of *Scelidosarus*. It is shown feeding along a Jurassic seashore where the shells of ammonites have been washed up. A flood might explain why the remains of this rare dinosuaur turn up in maritime sediments.

# STONEBARROW BEACH

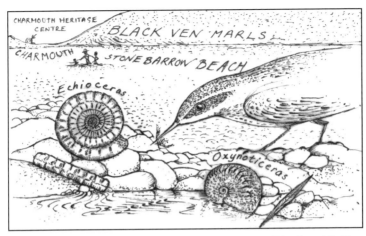

Stonebarrow Beach is famous for fine ammonites made up of "fool's gold". *They settle amongst the shingle a long way from the dangerous cliffs from which they are derived.*

The Black Ven Marls forms the base of the cliffs immediately to the east of the river Char for a distance of about one mile, taking in the full length of Stonebarrow Hill. The beach below this hill is renowned for pyritised ammonites derived from the Marls. These heavy fossils are continually washed out the cliffs and settle amongst the shingle where they are naturally sought after by families enjoying a holiday in the area.

Several types of these beautiful fossils can be found, notably the Proms that we have already considered and in particular an ammonite called *Echioceras* or "**Echi**" for short. You might mistake it for a Prom but the Echi grew larger, the coils of the shell were less tightly knit, and the rim of the shell was bounded by a faint keel. A very different ammonite that occasionally turns up is *Oxynoticeras* ("**Oxy**" for short). Its shell is a flat disc with a sharp perimeter from which its gets it name (Oxy is the Greek word for sharp). It is embossed with delicate ribs that are sickle-shaped and its suture lines are much more complicated than those of Proms and Echies.

*There is a vast amount of shingle to explore beneath Stonebarrow Hill and this can be done in safety well away from the cliffs under appropriate tide conditions.* The beach is exposed to the full force of winds which can blow up suddenly and i advisable to pack a windcheater even if the weather is fine. During periods of settled weather much of the shingle is often covered over by sand and pyritised ammonites are harder to find, but the beaches contain plenty of rolled framents of limestone covered with impressions of ammonites. These pebbles stand out well against the sand and make delightful souvenirs if not intriguing paperweights.

The further you go along Charmouth Beach the more likely you are to find belemnites. In due course these are the commonest fossils to be found as the Belemnite Marls descends to the shore. *By then you will be about a mile away from Charmouth and you should consider going back, especially if the tide is coming in!* is possible to scale the cliffs at a point known as St. Gabriel's Mouth and return ove the cliffs to Charmouth but this involves a hair-raising ascent up a crumbling ridge.

# SEATOWN

The cliffs around Seatown are crumpled up but the strata soon level out to the west with the top of the Belemnite Marls and the overlying Green Ammonite Beds forming the base of the cliffs. Fossils in a fair state of preservation derived from both formations then become common amongst the shingle which normally covers the beach. During rough weather the beach is sometimes swept clear of shingle and the fossil-rich top of the Belemnite Marls is exposed. However, for most of the year this "**Belemnite Pavement**", as we might call it, is covered over and it is not until you approach Golden Cap that you are quaranteed clear patches of limestone and shale studded with so many belemnites that they look as if someone had sprinkled nails over layers of quick-setting cement. The majority of these belemnites are of the robust bullet type, but a careful search should reward you with the remains of a thin and delicate torpedo-shaped belemnite to add to your collection.

The Belemnite Marls contains plenty of ammonites and bivalved molluscs but most of them are poorly preserved in contrast to many ammonites in the Green Ammonite Beds. This formation gets its name from the greenish crystals of calcite that often fill the air chambers of its ammonites. Many of the ammonites are contained in hard nodules about the size of cricket balls and these make very attractive ornaments when sawn across and polished. The ammonites are of two types: species of *Androgynoceras* and *Tragophylloceras*, "**Androgs**" and "**Trags**" for short. The shells of Androgs have very pronounced and widely spaced ribs and look like miniature goat horns. In contrast, the shells of Trags are smooth and flat, not unlike saucer-sized "Oxies" but with rounded rather than sharp edges.

The nodules containing these ammonites are difficult to find. Much more common are loose and related species washed out of marl. Their body chambers are plentiful at the foot of Golden Cap where they become trapped amongst the shingle and between boulders. The ribs of Androgs are soon worn down, however, and typical specimens look like curved white sausages that are easy to spot against the chocolate coloured debris of impure "fool's gold" that carpets the seashore.

The inner coils of an Androg are soon destroyed by the sea, leaving behind the tougher body chamber which, in turn, is eventually reduced to a sausage-shaped lump. The specimens are pictured on a patch of the Belemnite Pavement, about a kilometre to the west of Seatown.

*If you have made it to the foot of Golden Cap then take care! You will be confronted with a sheer cliff face rising up from the seashore to well over six hundred feet making its top the highest point on the south coast of England. The cliff-face often splits into vertical slices which crash down on to the beach. There is also the danger of becoming cut off by the tides as you make your way back to Seatown.*

# BACK TO LYME REGIS

The sort of fossils that attract the eye are harder to find on the beaches to the east of Seatown. Particularly elusive is a famous fossil starfish or rather a delicate member of the starfish family known as a brittle star. It is mostly confined to the undersurface of a hard layer of sandstone about four feet thick situated high in the cliffs between Seatown and the next river mouth along the Jurassic Coast (Eype's Mouth). This layer of sandstone is known as the **starfish bed** and although blocks of it fall upside down on to the seashore the fossils are soon chiselled out by local collectors.

Compacted but softer Jurassic sands make up the bulk of the vertical yellow cliffs to the east of West Bay and although these sands are poor in fossils they are topped by a band of stone which is full of them. This stone is about twelve feet thick and the fossils are mostly buried in a matrix of tiny granules which resemble the eggs (roe) of fish. Blocks of it fall on to the beaches, notably beneath Burton Cliffs.

The fossils are easy to make out but you will need a hammer and chisel to extract them. *The beaches around West Bay are therefore the province of the experienced fossil hunter equipped with appropriate safety gear rather than of the casual visitoir in persuit of educating and entertaining his children.*

Further east the cliffs give way to Chesil Beach as the major frontage of the Jurassic Coast. This beach is an enormous embankment of eighteen miles of shingle behind which is a lagoon known as The Fleet. Fossils can be picked up on the northern banks of the Fleet but access points are few and far between.

Chesil beach links up with Portland, an island famous for a band of fine and durable Jurassic limestone (Portland Stone) used, for instance by Sir Christopher Wren in rebuilding London after its disastrous fire of 1666.

Portland is too far away from Lyme Regis to come within the scope of this booklet – with one curious exception; the Cobb was slabbed over during the beginning of the nineteenth century with a very tough rock hewn out of the island. This rock, known as **Roach**, is riddled with holes where Jurassic shells have dissolved out. The fossilized internal mould of the tapering shell of a marine snail, *Aptyxiella portlandica* is extremely common in the stone. It looks like a cork-screw and is known to the quarrymen as "The Portland screw". Also very common are the moulds a molluscan bivalve, *Laevitrigonia gibbosa*, the "horses heads" of the quarrymen. The shell o this species is covered with a network of raised pimples. Most its fossils are external moulds which are pitted with impressions of the pimples, making the shellfish easy to identify.

The utility of roach as a material for sea defenses has as much to do with its cavities as the hardness of its matrix; much of the energy of waves bashing the Cobb is dissipated though its tunnels. Roach was used to top some of the walls of the town's eastern sea defence system built in 1996. It is instructive to compare the state of this stone with that of the Cobb. Two centuries separate the times when Roach was quarried out for use at these sites. During this period the Cobb has been trampelled over by millions of feet and yet its roach is almost as good as new. It has stood the test of time and like the fossils you have collected it will outlive you!

– THE END –